Biology for the Rhetoric Stage

Biology for the Rhetoric Stage

First Edition, 2016

Copyright @ Elemental Science, Inc.

Email: info@elementalscience.com

ISBN # 978-1-935614-50-0

Printed in the USA for worldwide distribution

For more copies write to:
Elemental Science
755 Grand Blvd B105 #218
Miramar Beach, FL 32550
info@elementalscience.com

Unit 1: Overview of Study

Introduction

Unit 1: Cell Structure, Function, and Reproduction

Unit 2: Genetics and Evolution

Unit 3: Ecology, Eukaryotes, and Plant Life

Unit 4: Animals and the Human Body

Appendix

Introduction to the Parents

In *Success in Science: A Manual for Excellence in Science Education*, we state that the high school student is "a law student. They have access to a great deal of organized, filed away information, but they are still learning the advanced techniques, as well a learning when to use the material and how to apply it."[1] The goals of science instruction at the rhetoric level are to make sure that the students know and understand the key principles and laws at work in science, and to teach them how to relate what they have learned to what they see around them. *Biology for the Rhetoric Stage* integrates the above goals into high school science instruction, as suggested in our book.

Textbook

For this study, we have chosen to use a widely available, standard text book, *CK-12 Biology*. You can download this text or read it online here:

🖥 http://www.ck12.org/book/CK-12-Biology/

The students will complete their reading assignment and then answer several of the questions from the text. Their answers should be added to the reading section of their science notebooks. They will also define several of the key terms from the chapter, which should be added to the glossary section of their notebook.

Experiment

Almost all of the experiments come from Late Nite Labs, an excellent program for online labs. Access can be purchased through our website:

🖥 http://elementalscience.com

At the end of each unit, the student will complete a full lab report for one of the experiments. An article explaining what a full lab report is can be found in the Appendix on pg. 113.

There are several weeks where there is no Late Nite Lab; instead, we have scheduled a hands-on experiment for the students to complete. Here is a list of the supplies you will need for these weeks:

- ✓ Unit 2 Week 3 - A piece of banana or strawberry, Dish soap, Salt, Ice-cold Isopropyl alcohol (70% or higher), Zipper-style plastic bag, Coffee filter, Funnel, Wooden coffee stirrer, Clear glass
- ✓ Unit 3 Week 3 - Posterboard

We have also included optional hands-on experiments for each week. You can see a list of the supplies you will need for these in the Appendix on pg. 121.

---

[1]Bradley R. Hudson and Paige Hudson, *Success in Science: A Manual for Excellence in Science Education* (Elemental Science, 2012), 86

Events in Science

This guide gives two options for the Events in Science section. One will familiarize the students with current events in science as they research on the internet for the various topics. The other will familiarize the students with the key historical figures in biology. We recommend that you choose one or the other to assign your students, as completing both options will be quite a lot of additional work.

Possible Schedules

You should expect the students to take approximately 5 to 6 hours each week to complete the given work. We have included two possible schedules for your reference: a two-days-a-week and a five-days-a-week schedule. Please feel free to alter this to suit each student's needs.

The Science Notebook

This year, the students will each create their own science notebooks. Each notebook should contain the following sections:

- 📖 Reading - This section of the notebook will contain any notes the students have taken, along with the answers to the questions the students are assigned each week.
- 📖 Lab - This section of the notebook will house the student's notes from the experiments they have done, along with any other materials relating to the labs.
- 📖 Events - This section of the notebook will include either the current events article summaries or the historical reports the student has done.
- 📖 Glossary - This section of the notebooking will have the definitions for the assigned vocabulary words.

The student can use a composition book and divide it into the required sections or use a three-ring binder with dividers for the science notebook.

Grading and Credits

This course meets the requirements for a full credit of high school biology or a full credit of lab science, depending upon which your student needs. Each week, the student will answer questions and define vocabulary that can count towards a class work grade for the course. For each lab, the student will complete a multiple choice section, which you can use for the lab grade for the course. At the end of each unit, we have included a unit exam, which you can use for the exam grade for the course. We suggest you use the following percentages to come up with a final grade for the course:

- ☞ Class work: 35 %
- ☞ Lab Grade: 35 %
- ☞ Exams: 30 %

Note - The multiple choice sections from the lab are graded automatically through Lab Nite Labs. The answers for the exams can be found on pg. 125 of the Appendix in this guide and a grading rubric for the Scientist Biography Reports can be found on pg. 127 of the Appendix.

Science-Oriented Students

If you have a student who plans to go on to major in the sciences, we suggest that you add an in-depth project and a research report to this program. An explanation of the in-depth project can be found on pg. 116 of the Appendix in this guide. An explanation of the research report can be found on pg. 117 of the Appendix in this guide.

Final Thoughts

If you find that this program contains too much work, please tailor it to the needs of your students. As the authors and publishers of this curriculum, we encourage you to contact us with any questions or problems that you might have concerning *Biology for the Rhetoric Stage* at support@elementalscience.com. We will be more than happy to answer you as soon as we are able. We trust that you and your students will enjoy *Biology for the Rhetoric Stage*!

Introduction to the Students

Welcome to Biology! This year you will learn about biochemistry, cell structure, photosynthesis, genetics, plants, microorganisms, anatomy, and much more. In this guide, you will find assignment sheets for each week. Each sheet is divided into four sections - textbook, experiments, events in science, and possible schedules. Let's look closer at each one:

- ✍ Textbook - For this study, we have chosen to use a widely available, standard text book, *CK-12 Biology*. You will complete your reading assignment and then answer several of the questions from the text. You will also define several of the key terms from the chapter.

- ☞ Experiment - The experiments in the program are almost all virtual. These come from Late Nite Labs, an excellent program for online experiments. Within this virtual lab, you will find background information for each lab, the procedure, and space for you to take notes.

- 🕐 Events in Science - There are two options for the Events in Science section. One will familiarize you with current events in science as you research on the internet for the various topics. The other will familiarize you with the key historical figures in biology. Please check with your teacher to see which option you would be expected to complete.

- ☐ Possible Schedules - You should count on taking approximately 5 to 6 hours each week to complete the given work in this course. We have included two possible schedules for your reference: a two-days-a-week and a five-days-a-week schedule. Please feel free to alter this to suit your needs.

The Science Notebook

This year, you will create a science notebook containing your work from the course. The notebook should contain the following sections:

- 📖 Reading - This section of the notebook will contain any notes you have taken, along with the answers to the questions you have been assigned each week.
- 📖 Lab - This section of the notebook will house your notes from the experiments you have done, along with any other materials relating to the labs.
- 📖 Events - This section of the notebook will include either the current events article summaries or the historical reports you have done.
- 📖 Glossary - This section of the notebooking will have the definitions for the assigned vocabulary words.

You can use a composition book and divide it into the required sections or use a three-ring binder with dividers for your science notebook.

Final Thoughts

We hope that you will enjoy your journey through biology with *Biology for the Rhetoric Stage*. If you have any questions or problems as you complete the work in this program, please email us at support@elementalscience.com. We will be more than happy to answer them as soon as we are able.

Biology for the Rhetoric Stage

Unit 1 - Cell Structure, Function, and Reproduction

Unit 1: Cell Structure, Function, and Reproduction

Overview of Study

Notes

Week 1 Assignment Sheet - Introduction to Biology

Textbook Assignments
Reading
📖 *CK-12 Biology* Sections 1.1, 1.2, 1.3
Written
After you finish reading, answer questions #1-6 in section 1.3 and file your work in the reading section of your science notebook. Then, define the following terms in the glossary section of your science notebook:

☐ Dependent variable   ☐ Stage
☐ Independent variable   ☐ Turret
☐ Scientific theory   ☐ Aperture
☐ Scientific law   ☐ Rheostat

Experiment - Introduction to the Virtual Biology Lab
Purpose
The purpose of this lab is to familiarize you with how a virtual lab works and to get you comfortable with using Late Nite Labs.
Pre-Reading
〰 Read the background and procedure sections for the "Introduction to Virtual Biology Labs" lab in Late Nite Labs.
Procedure
✓ Do the lab entitled "Introduction to Virtual Biology Labs" in Late Nite Labs.
Lab Notebook
☞ Write down on a sheet of paper or type out your notes in Late Nite Labs as you do the experiment. After you are done, print out your lab notes and add them to the lab section of your science notebook.
Lab Exam
⚡ Complete the multiple choice section of the "Introduction to Virtual Biology Labs" lab in Late Nite Labs. Submit the grade to your teacher.
Optional Hands-on
✂ Practice using a microscope by making wet mount and dry mount slides. Directions can be found here: http://elementalblogging.com/using-microscope-for-homeschool-science/.

Events in Science
Current Events
🕐 Find a current events article relating to the field of biochemistry and complete the article summary sheet found on pg. 131 of the Appendix. Once you are done, add the sheet to

Biology for the Rhetoric Stage Unit 1 - Weekly Assignment Sheets

the events section of your science notebook.

Historical Figures

🕑 Begin to research the life and work of Aristotle, who is considered by many to be the father of biology. You will have three weeks to complete your research. After that, you will have two weeks to prepare a two to three page paper on this scientist and his contributions to the field of biology.

Possible Schedules

Two Days a Week

Day 1	Day 2
❏ Read *CK-12 Biology* Sections 1.1 and 1.2. ❏ Add the vocabulary to the glossary section of your science notebook. ❏ Read the background and procedure sections for the week's lab. ❏ Do the current events assignment and add the sheet to the events section of your science notebook.	❏ Read *CK-12 Biology* Section 1.3. ❏ Answer the assigned questions in the reading section of your science notebook. ❏ Do the "Intro to Virtual Biology Labs" lab in Late Nite Labs. ❏ Record what you have done in the lab section of your science notebook and complete your lab exam for the week.

Five Days a Week

Day 1	Day 2	Day 3	Day 4	Day 5
❏ Read *CK-12 Biology* Sections 1.1 and 1.2. ❏ Add the vocabulary to the glossary section of your science notebook.	❏ Read *CK-12 Biology* Section 1.3. ❏ Answer the assigned questions in the reading section of your science notebook.	❏ Read the background and procedure sections for the week's lab.	❏ Do the "Intro to Virtual Biology Labs" lab in Late Nite Labs. ❏ Record what you have done in the lab section of your science notebook.	❏ Complete your lab exam for the week. ❏ Do the optional Hands-on Assignment.

Throughout the Week

❏ Choose one of the Events in Science assignments to do and add your work to the events section of your science notebook.

Week 2 Assignment Sheet - Chemistry of Life, part 1

Textbook Assignments
Reading
📖 *CK-12 Biology* Sections 2.1, 2.2

Written
After you finish reading, answer questions #1-7 in section 2.1 and file your work in the reading section of your science notebook. Then, define the following terms in the glossary section of your science notebook:

- [ ] Amino Acid
- [ ] Carbohydrate
- [ ] Complementary Base Pair
- [ ] DNA
- [ ] Lipid

- [ ] Monosaccharide
- [ ] Polysaccharide
- [ ] RNA
- [ ] Anabolic Reaction
- [ ] Catabolic Reaction

Experiment - Scientific Method
Purpose
The purpose of this lab is to familiarize you with how to use scientific methods to investigate a phenomenon.

Pre-Reading
⌒ Read the background and procedure sections for the "Scientific Method" lab in Late Nite Labs.

Procedure
✓ Do the lab entitled "Scientific Method" in Late Nite Labs.

Lab Notebook
☞ Write down on a sheet of paper or type out your notes in Late Nite Labs as you do the experiment. After you are done, print out your lab notes and add them to the lab section of your science notebook.

Lab Exam
🔩 Complete the multiple choice section of the "Scientific Method" lab in Late Nite Labs. Submit the grade to your teacher.

Optional Hands-on
✂ Learn about how complimentary base pairs work by creating a DNA ladder out of Legos. Directions can be found here: http://elementalblogging.com/homeschool-science-corner-dna/.

Events in Science
Current Events
🕐 Find a current events article relating to the field of biochemistry and complete the article

summary sheet found on pg. 131 of the Appendix. Once you are done, add the sheet to the events section of your science notebook.

Historical Figures

🕐 Continue to research the life and work of Aristotle.

Possible Schedules

Two Days a Week

Day 1	Day 2
❏ Read *CK-12 Biology* Section 2.1.	❏ Read *CK-12 Biology* Section 2.2.
❏ Add the vocabulary to the glossary section of your science notebook.	❏ Answer the assigned questions in the reading section of your science notebook.
❏ Read the background and procedure sections for the week's lab.	❏ Do the "Scientific Method" lab in Late Nite Labs.
❏ Do the current events assignment and add the sheet to the events section of your science notebook.	❏ Record what you have done in the lab section of your science notebook and complete your lab exam for the week.

Five Days a Week

Day 1	Day 2	Day 3	Day 4	Day 5
❏ Read *CK-12 Biology* Section 2.1. ❏ Add the vocabulary to the glossary section of your science notebook.	❏ Read *CK-12 Biology* Section 2.2. ❏ Answer the assigned questions in the reading section of your science notebook.	❏ Read the background and procedure sections for the week's lab.	❏ Do the "Scientific Method" lab in Late Nite Labs. ❏ Record what you have done in the lab section of your science notebook.	❏ Complete your lab exam for the week. ❏ Do the optional Hands-on Assignment.

Throughout the Week
❏ Choose one of the Events in Science assignments to do and add your work to the events section of your science notebook.

Week 3 Assignment Sheet - Chemistry of Life, part 2

Textbook Assignments

Reading
📖 *CK-12 Biology* Section 2.3

Written
After you finish reading, answer questions #1-6 in section 2.3 and file your work in the reading section of your science notebook. Then, define the following terms in the glossary section of your science notebook:

- ☐ Acid
- ☐ Base
- ☐ pH
- ☐ Polarity

Experiment - Acids, Bases, and pH Buffers

Purpose
The purpose of this lab is to understand the relationships between acids and bases, as well as to become familiar with measuring pH.

Pre-Reading
∽ Read the background and procedure sections for the "Acids, Bases, and pH Buffers" lab in Late Nite Labs.

Procedure
✓ Do the lab entitled "Acids, Bases, and pH Buffers" in Late Nite Labs.

Lab Notebook
☞ Write down on a sheet of paper or type out your notes in Late Nite Labs as you do the experiment. After you are done, print out your lab notes and add them to the lab section of your science notebook.

Lab Exam
⚡ Complete the multiple choice section of the "Acids, Bases, and pH Buffers" lab in Late Nite Labs. Submit the grade to your teacher.

Optional Hands-on
✂ Test common household materials to see if they are acids or bases. Directions can be found here: http://elementalblogging.com/science-corner-kitchen-acid-test/.

Events in Science

Current Events
🕐 Find a current events article relating to the field of biochemistry and complete the article summary sheet found on pg. 131 of the Appendix. Once you are done, add the sheet to the events section of your science notebook.

Historical Figures
🕐 Continue to research the life and work of Aristotle.

Possible Schedules

Two Days a Week

Day 1	Day 2
❏ Read *CK-12 Biology* Section 2.3. ❏ Add the vocabulary to the glossary section of your science notebook. ❏ Answer the assigned questions in the reading section of your science notebook. ❏ Do the current events assignment and add the sheet to the events section of your science notebook.	❏ Read the background and procedure sections for the week's lab. ❏ Do the "Acids, Bases, and pH Buffers" lab in Late Nite Labs. ❏ Record what you have done in the lab section of your science notebook and complete your lab exam for the week.

Five Days a Week

Day 1	Day 2	Day 3	Day 4	Day 5
❏ Read *CK-12 Biology* Section 2.3. ❏ Add the vocabulary to the glossary section of your science notebook.	❏ Answer the assigned questions in the reading section of your science notebook.	❏ Read the background and procedure sections for the week's lab.	❏ Do the "Acids, Bases, and pH Buffers" lab in Late Nite Labs. ❏ Record what you have done in the lab section of your science notebook.	❏ Complete your lab exam for the week. ❏ Do the optional Hands-on Assignment.

Throughout the Week

❏ Choose one of the Events in Science assignments to do and add your work to the events section of your science notebook.

Week 4 Assignment Sheet - Cell Structure and Function, part 1

Textbook Assignments

Reading
📖 *CK-12 Biology* Sections 3.1, 3.2

Written
After you finish reading, answer questions #1-3 in section 3.1 and questions #1-4 in section 3.2. File your work in the reading section of your science notebook. Then, define the following terms in the glossary section of your science notebook:

- ☐ Cytoplasm
- ☐ Organelle
- ☐ Plasma membrane
- ☐ Prokaryotic cell
- ☐ Ribosome

- ☐ Virus
- ☐ Endoplasmic reticulum
- ☐ Golgi apparatus
- ☐ Mitochondria
- ☐ Phospholipid bilayer

Experiment - Cell Structure and Function

Purpose
The purpose of this lab is to learn microscope techniques while exploring basic cellular structures.

Pre-Reading
✍ Read the background and procedure sections for the "Cell Structure and Function" lab in Late Nite Labs.

Procedure
✓ Do the lab entitled "Cell Structure and Function" in Late Nite Labs.

Lab Notebook
☞ Write down on a sheet of paper or type out your notes in Late Nite Labs as you do the experiment. After you are done, print out your lab notes and add them to the lab section of your science notebook.

Lab Exam
⚡ Complete the multiple choice section of the "Cell Structure and Function" lab in Late Nite Labs. Submit the grade to your teacher.

Optional Hands-on
✂ Make a Jell-O model of a cell. Use a margarine container for the cell membrane, Jell-O for cytoplasm, a grape for the nucleus and use your imagination for materials for the remaining organelles.

Events in Science

Current Events
🕐 Find a current events article relating to the field of biochemistry and complete the article

summary sheet found on pg. 131 of the Appendix. Once you are done, add the sheet to the events section of your science notebook.

Historical Figures

🕐 Begin to work on your paper on the life and work of Aristotle. This week, aim to complete your outline and rough draft. See pg. 118 in the Appendix for more directions. You will have three weeks to complete this paper.

Possible Schedules

Two Days a Week

Day 1	Day 2
❑ Read *CK-12 Biology* Section 3.1.	❑ Read *CK-12 Biology* Section 3.2.
❑ Add the vocabulary to the glossary section of your science notebook.	❑ Answer the assigned questions in the reading section of your science notebook.
❑ Read the background and procedure sections for the week's lab.	❑ Do the "Cell Structure and Function" lab in Late Nite Labs.
❑ Do the current events assignment and add the sheet to the events section of your science notebook.	❑ Record what you have done in the lab section of your science notebook and complete your lab exam for the week.

Five Days a Week

Day 1	Day 2	Day 3	Day 4	Day 5
❑ Read *CK-12 Biology* Section 3.1.	❑ Read *CK-12 Biology* Section 3.2.	❑ Read the background and procedure sections for the week's lab.	❑ Do the "Cell Structure and Function" lab in Late Nite Labs.	❑ Complete your lab exam for the week.
❑ Add the vocabulary to the glossary section of your science notebook.	❑ Answer the assigned questions in the reading section of your science notebook.		❑ Record what you have done in the lab section of your science notebook.	❑ Do the optional Hands-on Assignment.

Throughout the Week
❑ Choose one of the Events in Science assignments to do and add your work to the events section of your science notebook.

Week 5 Assignment Sheet - Cell Structure and Function, part 2

Textbook Assignments
Reading
📖 *CK-12 Biology* Section 3.3

Written
After you finish reading, answer questions #1-4 in section 3.3 and file your work in the reading section of your science notebook. Then, define the following terms in the glossary section of your science notebook:

☐ Active transport   ☐ Exocytosis
☐ Diffusion   ☐ Osmosis
☐ Endocytosis

Experiment - Diffusion and Osmosis
Purpose
The purpose of this lab is to explain the roles of diffusion and osmosis in cell transport.

Pre-Reading
☙ Read the background and procedure sections for the "Diffusion and Osmosis" lab in Late Nite Labs.

Procedure
✓ Do the lab entitled "Diffusion and Osmosis" in Late Nite Labs.

Lab Notebook
☞ Write down on a sheet of paper or type out your notes in Late Nite Labs as you do the experiment. After you are done, print out your lab notes and add them to the lab section of your science notebook.

Lab Exam
⚡ Complete the multiple choice section of the "Diffusion and Osmosis" lab in Late Nite Labs. Submit the grade to your teacher.

Optional Hands-on
✂ See osmosis in action using a gummy bear. Place one gummy bear into a glass of water and let it sit overnight. The next morning, take it out and compare the size to a gummy bear right out of the package.

Events in Science
Current Events
🕐 Find a current events article relating to the field of biochemistry and complete the article summary sheet found on pg. 131 of the Appendix. Once you are done, add the sheet to the events section of your science notebook.

Historical Figures

🕐 Continue to work on your paper on the life and work of Aristotle. This week, aim to complete your final draft. See pg. 118 in the Appendix for more directions.

Possible Schedules

Two Days a Week

Day 1	Day 2
❐ Read *CK-12 Biology* Section 3.3. ❐ Add the vocabulary to the glossary section of your science notebook. ❐ Answer the assigned questions in the reading section of your science notebook. ❐ Do the current events assignment and add the sheet to the events section of your science notebook.	❐ Read the background and procedure sections for the week's lab. ❐ Do the "Diffusion and Osmosis" lab in Late Nite Labs. ❐ Record what you have done in the lab section of your science notebook and complete your lab exam for the week.

Five Days a Week

Day 1	Day 2	Day 3	Day 4	Day 5
❐ Read *CK-12 Biology* Section 3.3. ❐ Add the vocabulary to the glossary section of your science notebook.	❐ Answer the assigned questions in the reading section of your science notebook.	❐ Read the background and procedure sections for the week's lab.	❐ Do the "Diffusion and Osmosis" lab in Late Nite Labs. ❐ Record what you have done in the lab section of your science notebook.	❐ Complete your lab exam for the week. ❐ Do the optional Hands-on Assignment.

Throughout the Week
❐ Choose one of the Events in Science assignments to do and add your work to the events section of your science notebook.

Week 6 Assignment Sheet - Photosynthesis and Cellular Respiration, part 1

Textbook Assignments

Reading
📖 *CK-12 Biology* Sections 4.1, 4.2

Written
After you finish reading, answer questions #1-5 in section 4.1 and questions #1-6 in section 4.2. File your work in the reading section of your science notebook. Then, define the following terms in the glossary section of your science notebook:

- ☐ Autotroph
- ☐ Cellular respiration
- ☐ Heterotroph
- ☐ Calvin Cycle
- ☐ Chemosynthesis
- ☐ Grana
- ☐ Light reactions
- ☐ Thylakoid membrane

Experiment - Photosynthesis

Purpose
The purpose of this lab is to explain the process of photosynthesis and investigate the relationship between environmental factors and the rate of photosynthesis.

Pre-Reading
☞ Read the background and procedure sections for the "Photosynthesis" lab in Late Nite Labs.

Procedure
✓ Do the lab entitled "Photosynthesis" in Late Nite Labs.

Lab Notebook
☞ Write down on a sheet of paper or type out your notes in Late Nite Labs as you do the experiment. After you are done, print out your lab notes and add them to the lab section of your science notebook.

Lab Exam
🗲 Complete the multiple choice section of the "Photosynthesis" lab in Late Nite Labs. Submit the grade to your teacher.

Optional Hands-on
✂ See a bit of photosynthesis in action using a leaf and a bowl filled with water. Directions for this project can be found here: https://www.pinterest.com/pin/192036371587791960/.

Events in Science

Current Events
🕐 Find a current events article relating to the field of botany and complete the article

summary sheet found on pg. 131 of the Appendix. Once you are done, add the sheet to the events section of your science notebook.

Historical Figures

🕐 Begin to research the life and work of Antoni van Leeuwenhoek, who is considered by many to be the father of microscopy. You will have three weeks to complete your research. After that, you will have two weeks to prepare a two to three page paper on this scientist and his contributions to the field of biology.

Possible Schedules

Two Days a Week

Day 1	Day 2
❑ Read *CK-12 Biology* Section 4.1.	❑ Read *CK-12 Biology* Section 4.2.
❑ Add the vocabulary to the glossary section of your science notebook.	❑ Answer the assigned questions in the reading section of your science notebook.
❑ Read the background and procedure sections for the week's lab.	❑ Do the "Photosynthesis" lab in Late Nite Labs.
❑ Do the current events assignment and add the sheet to the events section of your science notebook.	❑ Record what you have done in the lab section of your science notebook and complete your lab exam for the week.

Five Days a Week

Day 1	Day 2	Day 3	Day 4	Day 5
❑ Read *CK-12 Biology* Section 4.1.	❑ Read *CK-12 Biology* Section 4.2.	❑ Read the background and procedure sections for the week's lab.	❑ Do the "Photosynthesis" lab in Late Nite Labs.	❑ Complete your lab exam for the week.
❑ Add the vocabulary to the glossary section of your science notebook.	❑ Answer the assigned questions in the reading section of your science notebook.		❑ Record what you have done in the lab section of your science notebook.	❑ Do the optional Hands-on Assignment.

Throughout the Week
❑ Choose one of the Events in Science assignments to do and add your work to the events section of your science notebook.

Week 7 Assignment Sheet - Photosynthesis and Cellular Respiration, part 2

Textbook Assignments

Reading
📖 *CK-12 Biology* Sections 4.3, 4.4

Written
After you finish reading, answer questions #1-7 in section 4.3 and questions #1-5 in section 4.4. File your work in the reading section of your science notebook. Then, define the following terms in the glossary section of your science notebook:

- ☐ Aerobic respiration
- ☐ Anaerobic respiration
- ☐ Glycolysis
- ☐ Krebs cycle
- ☐ Alcoholic fermentation
- ☐ Lactic fermentation

Experiment - Cellular Respiration

Purpose
The purpose of this lab is to compare aerobic and anaerobic respiration.

Pre-Reading
👉 Read the background and procedure sections for the "Cellular Respiration" lab in Late Nite Labs.

Procedure
✓ Do the lab entitled "Cellular Respiration" in Late Nite Labs.

Lab Notebook
☞ Write down on a sheet of paper or type out your notes in Late Nite Labs as you do the experiment. After you are done, print out your lab notes and add them to the lab section of your science notebook.

Lab Exam
🗲 Complete the multiple choice section of the "Cellular Respiration" lab in Late Nite Labs. Submit the grade to your teacher.

Optional Hands-on
✂ Watch yeast ferment sugar, which is an example of anaerobic respiration. Add a teaspoon of sugar to a cup of water and stir until the sugar dissolves. Then, sprinkle a teaspoon of yeast on the top and watch what happens.

Events in Science

Current Events
🕐 Find a current events article relating to the field of botany and complete the article summary sheet found on pg. 131 of the Appendix. Once you are done, add the sheet to

the events section of your science notebook.

Historical Figures

🕐 Continue to research the life and work of Antoni van Leeuwenhoek.

Possible Schedules

Two Days a Week

Day 1	Day 2
❑ Read *CK-12 Biology* Section 4.3.	❑ Read *CK-12 Biology* Section 4.4.
❑ Add the vocabulary to the glossary section of your science notebook.	❑ Answer the assigned questions in the reading section of your science notebook.
❑ Read the background and procedure sections for the week's lab.	❑ Do the "Cellular Respiration" lab in Late Nite Labs.
❑ Do the current events assignment and add the sheet to the events section of your science notebook.	❑ Record what you have done in the lab section of your science notebook and complete your lab exam for the week.

Five Days a Week

Day 1	Day 2	Day 3	Day 4	Day 5
❑ Read *CK-12 Biology* Section 4.3. ❑ Add the vocabulary to the glossary section of your science notebook.	❑ Read *CK-12 Biology* Section 4.4. ❑ Answer the assigned questions in the reading section of your science notebook.	❑ Read the background and procedure sections for the week's lab.	❑ Do the "Cellular Respiration" lab in Late Nite Labs. ❑ Record what you have done in the lab section of your science notebook.	❑ Complete your lab exam for the week. ❑ Do the optional Hands-on Assignment.

Throughout the Week
❑ Choose one of the Events in Science assignments to do and add your work to the events section of your science notebook.

Week 8 Assignment Sheet - Cell Cycles

Textbook Assignments

Reading
📖 *CK-12 Biology* Section 5.1

Written
After you finish reading, answer questions #1-6 in section 5.1 and file your work in the reading section of your science notebook. Then, define the following terms in the glossary section of your science notebook:

- ☐ Binary fission
- ☐ Cancer
- ☐ Cytokinesis
- ☐ Interphase
- ☐ Mitosis
- ☐ Tumor

Experiment - Mitosis and Meiosis

Purpose
The purpose of this lab is to explain the process of mitosis and observe cells during meiosis.

Pre-Reading
🖎 Read the background and procedure sections for the "Mitosis and Meiosis" lab in Late Nite Labs.

Procedure
✓ Do the lab entitled "Mitosis and Meiosis" in Late Nite Labs.

Lab Notebook
☞ Write down on a sheet of paper or type out your notes in Late Nite Labs as you do the experiment. After you are done, print out your lab notes and add them to the lab section of your science notebook.

Lab Exam
🗲 Complete the multiple choice section of the "Mitosis and Meiosis" lab in Late Nite Labs. Submit the grade to your teacher.

Optional Hands-on
✂ Dissect a haploid cell, a.k.a. an egg. Use the following website to identify the different parts of a chicken egg: http://imaginationstationtoledo.org/content/2011/04/the-anatomy-of-a-chicken-egg/.

Events in Science

Current Events
☺ Find a current events article relating to the field of molecular biology and complete the article summary sheet found on pg. 131 of the Appendix. Once you are done, add the sheet to the events section of your science notebook.

Historical Figures

🕐 Continue to research the life and work of Antoni van Leeuwenhoek.

Possible Schedules

Two Days a Week

Day 1	Day 2
❒ Read *CK-12 Biology* Section 5.1. ❒ Add the vocabulary to the glossary section of your science notebook. ❒ Answer the assigned questions in the reading section of your science notebook. ❒ Do the current events assignment and add the sheet to the events section of your science notebook.	❒ Read the background and procedure sections for the week's lab. ❒ Do the "Mitosis and Meiosis" lab in Late Nite Labs. ❒ Record what you have done in the lab section of your science notebook and complete your lab exam for the week.

Five Days a Week

Day 1	Day 2	Day 3	Day 4	Day 5
❒ Read *CK-12 Biology* Section 5.1. ❒ Add the vocabulary to the glossary section of your science notebook.	❒ Answer the assigned questions in the reading section of your science notebook.	❒ Read the background and procedure sections for the week's lab.	❒ Do the "Mitosis and Meiosis" lab in Late Nite Labs. ❒ Record what you have done in the lab section of your science notebook.	❒ Complete your lab exam for the week. ❒ Do the optional Hands-on Assignment.
Throughout the Week				
❒ Choose one of the Events in Science assignments to do and add your work to the events section of your science notebook.				

Week 9 Assignment Sheet - Mitosis

Textbook Assignments

Reading
📖 *CK-12 Biology* Section 5.2

Written
After you finish reading, answer questions #1-6 in section 5.2 and file your work in the reading section of your science notebook. Then, define the following terms in the glossary section of your science notebook:

☐ Anaphase   ☐ Homologous chromosomes
☐ Centromere   ☐ Metaphase
☐ Chromatid   ☐ Prophase
☐ Chromatin   ☐ Telophase

Experiment - Full Lab Report

Lab Notebook
☞ This week, choose one of your previous labs and begin to write a full lab report. See pg. 113 for directions on how to write a full lab report. You will have two weeks to complete your write-up.

Optional Hands-on
✂ Make a poster depicting the different phases of mitosis using pipe cleaners for your chromosomes.

Events in Science

Current Events
🕑 Find a current events article relating to the field of molecular biology and complete the article summary sheet found on pg. 131 of the Appendix. Once you are done, add the sheet to the events section of your science notebook.

Historical Figures
🕑 Begin to work on your paper on the life and work of Antoni van Leeuwenhoek. This week, aim to complete your outline and rough draft. See pg. 118 in the Appendix for more directions. You will have three weeks to complete this paper.

Possible Schedules

Two Days a Week

Day 1	Day 2
❏ Read *CK-12 Biology* Section 5.2. ❏ Add the vocabulary to the glossary section of your science notebook. ❏ Answer the assigned questions in the reading section of your science notebook.	❏ Work on the full Lab Report. ❏ Do the current events assignment and add the sheet to the events section of your science notebook.

Five Days a Week

Day 1	Day 2	Day 3	Day 4	Day 5
❏ Read *CK-12 Biology* Section 5.2. ❏ Add the vocabulary to the glossary section of your science notebook.	❏ Answer the assigned questions in the reading section of your science notebook.	❏ Work on the full Lab Report.	❏ Work on the full Lab Report.	❏ Do the optional Hands-on Assignment.

Throughout the Week
❏ Choose one of the Events in Science assignments to do and add your work to the events section of your science notebook.

Week 10 Assignment Sheet - Meiosis

Textbook Assignments
Reading
📖 *CK-12 Biology* Section 5.3

Written
After you finish reading, answer questions #1-7 in section 5.3 and file your work in the reading section of your science notebook. Then, define the following terms in the glossary section of your science notebook:

☐ Crossing-over	☐ Haploid
☐ Diploid	☐ Independent Assortment
☐ Fertilization	☐ Meiosis
☐ Gamete	☐ Sexual reproduction
☐ Gametogenesis	☐ Zygote

Experiment - Full Lab Report
Lab Notebook
☞ This week, finish writing the full lab report. See pg. 113 for directions on how to write a full lab report. Add your completed write-up to your lab notebook.

Optional Hands-on
✂ Make a poster depicting the different phases of meiosis using pipe cleaners for your chromosomes.

Events in Science
Current Events
☉ Find a current events article relating to the field of molecular biology and complete the article summary sheet found on pg. 131 of the Appendix. Once you are done, add the sheet to the events section of your science notebook.

Historical Figures
☉ Continue to work on your paper on the life and work of Antoni van Leeuwenhoek. This week, aim to complete your final draft. See pg. 118 in the Appendix for more directions.

Possible Schedules

Two Days a Week

Day 1	Day 2
❑ Read *CK-12 Biology* Section 5.3. ❑ Add the vocabulary to the glossary section of your science notebook. ❑ Read the background and procedure sections for the week's lab. ❑ Answer the assigned questions in the reading section of your science notebook.	❑ Finish the full Lab Report. ❑ Do the current events assignment and add the sheet to the events section of your science notebook.

Five Days a Week

Day 1	Day 2	Day 3	Day 4	Day 5
❑ Read *CK-12 Biology* Section 5.3. ❑ Add the vocabulary to the glossary section of your science notebook.	❑ Answer the assigned questions in the reading section of your science notebook.	❑ Work on the full Lab Report.	❑ Finish the full Lab Report.	❑ Do the optional Hands-on Assignment.

Throughout the Week

❑ Choose one of the Events in Science assignments to do and add your work to the events section of your science notebook.

Unit 1 Test

1. Which step is not involved in the process of scientific investigation?

   a. Form A Hypothesis

   b. Ask A Question

   c. Test the Hypothesis

   d. Build a diagram

2. Which answer best defines the characteristics of all living things?

   a. 1. It responds to the environment.
      2. It grows and develops.
      3. It produces offspring.
      4. It maintains homeostasis.
      5. It has complex chemistry.
      6. It consists of cells.

   b. 1. It responds to the environment.
      2. It communicates with other species.
      3. It produces offspring.
      4. It maintains homeostasis.
      5. It has complex anatomy.
      6. It consists of cells.

   c. 1. It responds to the environment.
      2. It consumes.
      3. It produces offspring.
      4. It maintains homeostasis.
      5. It has complex chemistry.
      6. It consists of cells.

   d. 1. It responds to the environment.
      2. It grows and develops.
      3. It is motile.
      4. It maintains homeostasis.
      5. It has complex chemistry.
      6. It consists of cells.

3. There are four major types of organic compounds that we are aware of. Which of these is not a type of organic compound?

   a. Carbohydrates

   b. Lipids

c. Salts

d. Proteins

4. Every nucleotide is made up of three smaller compounds. Which list of compounds is correct?

   a. 1. Fatty acid
      2. Phosphate group
      3. Nitrogen base

   b. 1. DNA
      2. Phosphate group
      3. Nitrogen base

   c. 1. RNA
      2. Phosphate group
      3. Nitrogen base

   d. 1. Sugar
      2. Phosphate group
      3. Nitrogen base

5. Complete the equation for the breakdown of water: $2\ H_2O \rightarrow H_3O^+ +$ _____

   a. OH^-

   b. OH^+

   c. H_2^+

   d. O_2H_2

6. What causes the pH of pure water to be at 7 or neutral pH?

   a. A high hydronium concentration

   b. A high hydrogen ion concentration

   c. A balanced between the hydronium ion and hydrogen ion concentration

   d. A low hydrogen ion concentration

7. Why are most cells relatively small and do not continue to grow in size but instead divide?

   a. Cells do not have the space to expand larger

   b. Larger cells are less motile than smaller cells

   c. Cell surface area is larger in smaller cells, allowing more diffusion across the cell membrane

8. Which answer best describes the functions of the cytoplasm?

   a. 1. Suspending cell walls

2. Pushing against the plasma membrane to help the cell keep its shape

3. Providing a site for many of the biochemical reactions of the cell

b. 1. Suspending cell walls
2. Pushing against the organelles to help the cell keep its shape
3. Providing a site for many of the biochemical reactions of the cell

c. 1. Suspending cell organelles
2. Pushing against the plasma membrane to help the cell keep its shape
3. Nourishment for the organelles

d. 1. Suspending cell organelles
2. Pushing against the plasma membrane to help the cell keep its shape
3. Providing a site for many of the biochemical reactions of the cell

9. One example of cellular transport that occurs in cells is the transport of sodium and potassium across the cell membrane. This is an example of:

a. Active transport

b. Passive transport

c. Chemical transport

d. Biological transport

10. What are two types of vesicle transport?

a. Exocytosis, Endocytosis

b. Passive Transport, Active Transport

c. Chemical Transport, Biological Transport

d. Biochemical Transport, Motile Transport

11. What molecule is not involved in the production of energy for cells?

a. ATP

b. ADP

c. Glucose

d. Ribose

12. A chloroplast consists of all of these except:

a. Thylakoid membrane

b. Stroma

c. Chlorophyll

d. Mitochondria

13. In glycolysis, how many ATP molecules are made during this stage of cellular respiration?

  a. 4

  b. 6

  c. 5

  d. 3

14. What chemical below is the precursor for the Krebs cycle

  a. NAD+

  b. Acetyl-coA

  c. Pyruvic acid

  d. Citric acid

15. Which compound is not a byproduct of alcoholic fermentation?

  a. $2H_2O$

  b. 2NADH

  c. 2 ETHANOL

  d. $2CO_2$

16. What is not a step in binary fission?

  a. DNA Replication

  b. Chromosome Segregation

  c. Separation

  d. Spindle Formation

17. When does the cell check to make sure the DNA has been replicated properly?

  a. S phase

  b. G_1 phase

  c. Interphase

  d. Telophase

18. What are the four phases of mitosis, in order?

  a. Prophase, anaphase, metaphase, and telophase

  b. Prophase, metaphase, anaphase, and telophase

  c. Telophase, metaphase, anaphase, and prophase

19. During telophase, which step does not occur?

a. Chromosomes uncoil

b. Spindle breaks down

c. New nuclear membrane forms

d. Cytoplasm splits

20. During asexual reproduction, offspring are:

a. Identical genetically

b. Genetically similar

c. Genetically different

d. Genetic mutant

Biology for the Rhetoric Stage

Unit 2 - Genetics and Evolution

Unit 2: Genetics and Evolution

Overview of Study

Notes

Week 1 Assignment Sheet - Gregor Mendel and Genetics

Textbook Assignments
Reading
📖 *CK-12 Biology* Sections 6.1, 6.2

Written
After you finish reading, answer questions #1-7 in section 6.1 and questions #1-4 in section 6.2. File your work in the reading section of your science notebook. Then, define the following terms in the glossary section of your science notebook:

☐ Allele   ☐ Law of Independent Assortment
☐ Dominant allele   ☐ Phenotype
☐ Genotype   ☐ Recessive allele
☐ Heterozygote   ☐ Co-dominance
☐ Homozygote   ☐ Punnett square

Experiment - Expanded Diffusion and Osmosis
Purpose
The purpose of this lab is to explain the roles of diffusion and osmosis in cell transport.

Pre-Reading
✍ Read the background and procedure sections for the "Expanded Diffusion and Osmosis" lab in Late Nite Labs.

Procedure
✓ Do the lab entitled "Expanded Diffusion and Osmosis" in Late Nite Labs.

Lab Notebook
☞ Write down on a sheet of paper or type out your notes in Late Nite Labs as you do the experiment. After you are done, print out your lab notes and add them to the lab section of your science notebook.

Lab Exam
⚡ Complete the multiple choice section of the "Expanded Diffusion and Osmosis" lab in Late Nite Labs. Submit the grade to your teacher.

Optional Hands-on
✂ Practice creating a Punnett square with Legos and a worksheet. Directions for this can be found here: http://elementalblogging.com/punnett-square/.

Events in Science
Current Events
🕐 Find a current events article relating to the field of genetics and complete the article summary sheet found on pg. 131 of the Appendix. Once you are done, add the sheet to the events section of your science notebook.

Historical Figures

🕐 Begin to research the life and work of Gregor Mendel, who is considered by many to be the father of genetics. You will have three weeks to complete your research. After that, you will have two weeks to prepare a two to three page paper on this scientist and his contributions to the field of biology.

Possible Schedules

Two Days a Week

Day 1	Day 2
❐ Read *CK-12 Biology* Section 6.1.	❐ Read *CK-12 Biology* Section 6.2.
❐ Add the vocabulary to the glossary section of your science notebook.	❐ Answer the assigned questions in the reading section of your science notebook.
❐ Read the background and procedure sections for the week's lab.	❐ Do the "Expanded Diffusion and Osmosis" lab in Late Nite Labs.
❐ Do the current events assignment and add the sheet to the events section of your science notebook.	❐ Record what you have done in the lab section of your science notebook and complete your lab exam for the week.

Five Days a Week

Day 1	Day 2	Day 3	Day 4	Day 5
❐ Read *CK-12 Biology* Section 6.1. ❐ Add the vocabulary to the glossary section of your science notebook.	❐ Read *CK-12 Biology* Section 6.2. ❐ Answer the assigned questions in the reading section of your science notebook.	❐ Read the background and procedure sections for the week's lab.	❐ Do the "Expanded Diffusion and Osmosis" lab in Late Nite Labs. ❐ Record what you have done in the lab section of your science notebook.	❐ Complete your lab exam for the week. ❐ Do the optional Hands-on Assignment.

Throughout the Week
❐ Choose one of the Events in Science assignments to do and add your work to the events section of your science notebook.

Week 2 Assignment Sheet - Molecular Genetics, part 1

Textbook Assignments

Reading
📖 *CK-12 Biology* Sections 7.1, 7.2

Written
After you finish reading, answer questions #1-6 in section 7.1 and questions #1-4 in section 7.2. File your work in the reading section of your science notebook. Then, define the following terms in the glossary section of your science notebook:

- ☐ Chargaff's Rules
- ☐ mRNA
- ☐ rRNA
- ☐ tRNA
- ☐ Codon
- ☐ Transcription
- ☐ Translation

Experiment - Genetics of Corn

Purpose
The purpose of this lab is to explain Mendelian genetics and use experimental data to investigate Mendelian genetics.

Pre-Reading
↝ Read the background and procedure sections for the "Genetics of Corn" lab in Late Nite Labs.

Procedure
✓ Do the lab entitled "Genetics of Corn" in Late Nite Labs.

Lab Notebook
☞ Write down on a sheet of paper or type out your notes in Late Nite Labs as you do the experiment. After you are done, print out your lab notes and add them to the lab section of your science notebook.

Lab Exam
⚡ Complete the multiple choice section of the "Genetics of Corn" lab in Late Nite Labs. Submit the grade to your teacher.

Optional Hands-on
✂ Use Easter eggs and M&M's to practice genetic recombination. Directions for this project can be found here: http://science-mattersblog.blogspot.com/2011/04/genetics-easter-egg-genetics.html.

Events in Science

Current Events
🕑 Find a current events article relating to the field of genetics and complete the article summary sheet found on pg. 131 of the Appendix. Once you are done, add the sheet to

the events section of your science notebook.

Historical Figures

⏱ Continue to research the life and work of Gregor Mendel.

Possible Schedules

Two Days a Week

Day 1	Day 2
❏ Read *CK-12 Biology* Section 7.1.	❏ Read *CK-12 Biology* Section 7.2.
❏ Add the vocabulary to the glossary section of your science notebook.	❏ Answer the assigned questions in the reading section of your science notebook.
❏ Read the background and procedure sections for the week's lab.	❏ Do the "Genetics of Corn" lab in Late Nite Labs.
❏ Do the current events assignment and add the sheet to the events section of your science notebook.	❏ Record what you have done in the lab section of your science notebook and complete your lab exam for the week.

Five Days a Week

Day 1	Day 2	Day 3	Day 4	Day 5
❏ Read *CK-12 Biology* Section 7.1.	❏ Read *CK-12 Biology* Section 7.2.	❏ Read the background and procedure sections for the week's lab.	❏ Do the "Genetics of Corn" lab in Late Nite Labs.	❏ Complete your lab exam for the week.
❏ Add the vocabulary to the glossary section of your science notebook.	❏ Answer the assigned questions in the reading section of your science notebook.		❏ Record what you have done in the lab section of your science notebook.	❏ Do the optional Hands-on Assignment.

Throughout the Week

❏ Choose one of the Events in Science assignments to do and add your work to the events section of your science notebook.

Week 3 Assignment Sheet - Molecular Genetics, part 2

Textbook Assignments
Reading
📖 *CK-12 Biology* Sections 7.3, 7.4

Written
After you finish reading, answer questions #1-6 in section 7.3 and questions #1-4 in section 7.4. File your work in the reading section of your science notebook. Then, define the following terms in the glossary section of your science notebook:

- ☐ Chromosomal alteration
- ☐ Frameshift mutation
- ☐ Germline mutation
- ☐ Mutagen
- ☐ Point mutation
- ☐ Somatic mutation
- ☐ Homeobox gene
- ☐ Operon
- ☐ TATA box

Experiment - DNA Extraction
Purpose
The purpose of this lab is to extract DNA protein from a common fruit.

Pre-Reading
ᑛ No pre-reading for this week

Procedure
✓ Extract DNA from fruit. You will need a piece of banana or strawberry, dish soap, salt, ice-cold isopropyl alcohol (70% or higher), zipper-style plastic bag, coffee filter, funnel, wooden coffee stirrer, and a clear glass for the extraction process. Directions for this lab can be found here: http://sassafrasscience.com/extracting-dna-uncle-cecil/.

Lab Notebook
☞ Write down on a sheet of paper or type out your notes as you do the experiment. After you are done, add them to the lab section of your science notebook.

Lab Exam
⚡ There is no lab exam for this week.

Optional Hands-on
✂ Repeat the experiment with several different types of food or your own saliva.

Events in Science
Current Events
⏱ Find a current events article relating to the field of genetics and complete the article summary sheet found on pg. 131 of the Appendix. Once you are done, add the sheet to the events section of your science notebook.

Historical Figures

🕐 Continue to research the life and work of Gregor Mendel.

Possible Schedules

Two Days a Week

Day 1	Day 2
❑ Read *CK-12 Biology* Section 7.3. ❑ Add the vocabulary to the glossary section of your science notebook. ❑ Answer the assigned questions in the reading section of your science notebook.	❑ Read *CK-12 Biology* Section 7.4. ❑ Do the "DNA Extraction" lab. ❑ Record what you have done in the lab section of your science notebook. ❑ Do the current events assignment and add the sheet to the events section of your science notebook.

Five Days a Week

Day 1	Day 2	Day 3	Day 4	Day 5
❑ Read *CK-12 Biology* Section 7.3. ❑ Add the vocabulary to the glossary section of your science notebook.	❑ Read *CK-12 Biology* Section 7.4. ❑ Add the vocabulary to the glossary section of your science notebook.	❑ Answer the assigned questions in the reading section of your science notebook.	❑ Do the "DNA Extraction" lab. ❑ Record what you have done in the lab section of your science notebook.	❑ Do the optional Hands-on Assignment.

Throughout the Week
❑ Choose one of the Events in Science assignments to do and add your work to the events section of your science notebook.

Week 4 Assignment Sheet - Human Genetics

Textbook Assignments

Reading
📖 *CK-12 Biology* Sections 8.1, 8.2

Written
After you finish reading, answer questions #1-4 in section 8.1 and questions #1-4 in section 8.2. File your work in the reading section of your science notebook. Then, define the following terms in the glossary section of your science notebook:

- ☐ Autosome
- ☐ Human genome
- ☐ Linkage map
- ☐ Sex-linked gene
- ☐ X-linked gene
- ☐ Epistasis
- ☐ Non-disjunction
- ☐ Pleiotrophy

Experiment - DNA

Purpose
The purpose of this lab is to describe the structure and function of DNA, as well as to compare DNA samples for familial and non-familial similarities.

Pre-Reading
᪰ Read the background and procedure sections for the "DNA" lab in Late Nite Labs.

Procedure
✓ Do the lab entitled "DNA" in Late Nite Labs.

Lab Notebook
☞ Write down on a sheet of paper or type out your notes in Late Nite Labs as you do the experiment. After you are done, print out your lab notes and add them to the lab section of your science notebook.

Lab Exam
↯ Complete the multiple choice section of the "DNA" lab in Late Nite Labs. Submit the grade to your teacher.

Optional Hands-on
✂ Create a pictorial family tree. Under each picture, note the hair color and eye color of the individual. Then, follow those traits as they are passed down through the family.

Events in Science

Current Events
🕐 Find a current events article relating to the field of genetics and complete the article summary sheet found on pg. 131 of the Appendix. Once you are done, add the sheet to the events section of your science notebook.

Historical Figures

🕑 Begin to work on your paper on the life and work of Gregor Mendel. This week, aim to complete your outline and rough draft. See pg. 118 in the Appendix for more directions. You will have three weeks to complete this paper.

Possible Schedules

Two Days a Week

Day 1	Day 2
❏ Read *CK-12 Biology* Section 8.1. ❏ Add the vocabulary to the glossary section of your science notebook. ❏ Read the background and procedure sections for the week's lab. ❏ Do the current events assignment and add the sheet to the events section of your science notebook.	❏ Read *CK-12 Biology* Section 8.2. ❏ Answer the assigned questions in the reading section of your science notebook. ❏ Do the "DNA" lab in Late Nite Labs. ❏ Record what you have done in the lab section of your science notebook and complete your lab exam for the week.

Five Days a Week

Day 1	Day 2	Day 3	Day 4	Day 5
❏ Read *CK-12 Biology* Section 8.1. ❏ Add the vocabulary to the glossary section of your science notebook.	❏ Read *CK-12 Biology* Section 8.2. ❏ Answer the assigned questions in the reading section of your science notebook.	❏ Read the background and procedure sections for the week's lab.	❏ Do the "DNA" lab in Late Nite Labs. ❏ Record what you have done in the lab section of your science notebook.	❏ Complete your lab exam for the week. ❏ Do the optional Hands-on Assignment.

Throughout the Week

❏ Choose one of the Events in Science assignments to do and add your work to the events section of your science notebook.

Week 5 Assignment Sheet - Biotechnology

Textbook Assignments

Reading
📖 *CK-12 Biology* Section 8.3

Written
After you finish reading, answer questions #1-5 in section 8.3 and file your work in the reading section of your science notebook. Then, define the following terms in the glossary section of your science notebook:

- ☐ Biotechnology
- ☐ Genetic engineering
- ☐ Phramacogenomics
- ☐ Polymerase Chain Reaction (PCR)
- ☐ Transgenic crop

Experiment - Biology PCR

Purpose
The purpose of this lab is to practice modern molecular genetic techniques used for bacterial identification.

Pre-Reading
☞ Read the background and procedure sections for the "Biology PCR" lab in Late Nite Labs.

Procedure
✓ Do the lab entitled "Biology PCR" in Late Nite Labs.

Lab Notebook
☞ Write down on a sheet of paper or type out your notes in Late Nite Labs as you do the experiment. After you are done, print out your lab notes and add them to the lab section of your science notebook.

Lab Exam
↯ Complete the multiple choice section of the "Biology PCR" lab in Late Nite Labs. Submit the grade to your teacher.

Optional Hands-on
✂ Learn more about PCR reactions by watching the following 3-D animation: https://www.dnalc.org/resources/3d/19-polymerase-chain-reaction.html.

Events in Science

Current Events
🕐 Find a current events article relating to the field of biotechnology and complete the article summary sheet found on pg. 131 of the Appendix. Once you are done, add the sheet to the events section of your science notebook.

Historical Figures

🕐 Continue to work on your paper on the life and work of Gregor Mendel. This week, aim to complete your final draft. See pg. 118 in the Appendix for more directions.

Possible Schedules

Two Days a Week

Day 1	Day 2
❏ Read *CK-12 Biology* Section 8.3. ❏ Add the vocabulary to the glossary section of your science notebook. ❏ Answer the assigned questions in the reading section of your science notebook. ❏ Do the current events assignment and add the sheet to the events section of your science notebook.	❏ Read the background and procedure sections for the week's lab. ❏ Do the "Biology PCR" lab in Late Nite Labs. ❏ Record what you have done in the lab section of your science notebook and complete your lab exam for the week.

Five Days a Week

Day 1	Day 2	Day 3	Day 4	Day 5
❏ Read *CK-12 Biology* Section 8.3. ❏ Add the vocabulary to the glossary section of your science notebook.	❏ Answer the assigned questions in the reading section of your science notebook.	❏ Read the background and procedure sections for the week's lab.	❏ Do the "Biology PCR" lab in Late Nite Labs. ❏ Record what you have done in the lab section of your science notebook.	❏ Complete your lab exam for the week. ❏ Do the optional Hands-on Assignment.

Throughout the Week

❏ Choose one of the Events in Science assignments to do and add your work to the events section of your science notebook.

Week 6 Assignment Sheet - From the First Organism Onward

Textbook Assignments
Reading
📖 *CK-12 Biology* Sections 9.1, 9.2, 9.3

Written
After you finish reading, answer questions #1-3 in section 9.1, questions #5-6 in section 9.2, and questions #4-5 in section 9.3. File your work in the reading section of your science notebook. Then, define the following terms in the glossary section of your science notebook:

- ☐ Extinction
- ☐ Fossil record
- ☐ Last Universal Common Ancestor
- ☐ Cambrian explosion
- ☐ Mesozoic era
- ☐ Permian extinction
- ☐ Clade
- ☐ Linnean classification system

Experiment - Full Lab Report
Lab Notebook
☞ This week, choose one of your previous labs and begin to write a full lab report. See pg. 113 for directions on how to write a full lab report. You will have two weeks to complete your write-up.

Optional Hands-on
✂ Complete question #6 (creating your own Linnean classification system) in section 9.3.

Events in Science
Current Events
🕐 Find a current events article relating to the field of biotechnology and complete the article summary sheet found on pg. 131 of the Appendix. Once you are done, add the sheet to the events section of your science notebook.

Historical Figures
🕐 There is no historical figures assignment for this week.

Possible Schedules

Two Days a Week

Day 1	Day 2
❏ Read *CK-12 Biology* Sections 9.1 and 9.2. ❏ Add the vocabulary to the glossary section of your science notebook. ❏ Answer the assigned questions in the reading section of your science notebook.	❏ Read *CK-12 Biology* Section 9.3. ❏ Work on the full Lab Report. ❏ Do the current events assignment and add the sheet to the events section of your science notebook.

Five Days a Week

Day 1	Day 2	Day 3	Day 4	Day 5
❏ Read *CK-12 Biology* Sections 9.1 and 9.2. ❏ Add the vocabulary to the glossary section of your science notebook.	❏ Read *CK-12 Biology* Section 9.3. ❏ Answer the assigned questions in the reading section of your science notebook.	❏ Work on the full Lab Report.	❏ Work on the full Lab Report.	❏ Do the optional Hands-on Assignment.

Throughout the Week

❏ Choose one of the Events in Science assignments to do and add your work to the events section of your science notebook.

Week 7 Assignment Sheet - Theory of Evolution

Textbook Assignments

Reading
📖 *CK-12 Biology* Section 10.1, 10.2, 10.3, 10.4

Written
    After you finish reading, answer questions #1-7 in section 5.3 and file your work in the reading section of your science notebook. Then, define the following terms in the glossary section of your science notebook:

- ☐ Artificial selection
- ☐ Fitness
- ☐ Adaptive radiation
- ☐ Biogeography
- ☐ Homologous structure
- ☐ Vestigial structure

- ☐ Allele frequency
- ☐ Hardy-Weinberg theorem
- ☐ Macroevolution
- ☐ Microevolution
- ☐ Coevolution
- ☐ Speciation

Experiment - Full Lab Report

Lab Notebook
☞ This week, finish writing the full lab report. See pg. 113 for directions on how to write a full lab report. Add your completed write-up to your lab notebook.

Optional Late Nite Lab
✂ Complete the Late Nite Lab entitled "Evolution." This lab will introduce you to the concept of evolution through adaptive radiation and convergent evolution.

Optional Hands-on
✂ There is no optional hands-on activity for this week.

Events in Science

Current Events
🕐 Find a current events article relating to the field of biotechnology and complete the article summary sheet found on pg. 131 of the Appendix. Once you are done, add the sheet to the events section of your science notebook.

Historical Figures
🕐 There is no historical figures assignment for this week.

Possible Schedules

Two Days a Week

Day 1	Day 2
❑ Read *CK-12 Biology* Sections 10.1 and 10.2. ❑ Add the vocabulary to the glossary section of your science notebook. ❑ Answer the assigned questions in the reading section of your science notebook.	❑ Read *CK-12 Biology* Sections 10.3 and 10.4. ❑ Finish the full Lab Report. ❑ Do the current events assignment and add the sheet to the events section of your science notebook.

Five Days a Week

Day 1	Day 2	Day 3	Day 4	Day 5
❑ Read *CK-12 Biology* Sections 10.1 and 10.2. ❑ Add the vocabulary to the glossary section of your science notebook.	❑ Read *CK-12 Biology* Sections 10.3 and 10.4. ❑ Answer the assigned questions in the reading section of your science notebook.	❑ Work on the full Lab Report.	❑ Work on the full Lab Report.	❑ Finish the full Lab Report.

Throughout the Week

❑ Choose one of the Events in Science assignments to do and add your work to the events section of your science notebook.

Unit 2 Test

1. What did Gregor Mendel use for his first experiment study group?

    a. Potatoes

    b. Tomatoes

    c. Peas

    d. Grapes

2. What two laws did Gregor Mendel develop?

    a. Independent Assortment, Law of Segregation

    b. Dependent Assortment, Law of Segregation

    c. Independent Assortment, Law of Substitution

    d. Dependent Assortment, Law of Substitution

3. Co-dominance is when:

    a. Both alleles are expressed with recessive traits equally

    b. Both alleles are expressed equally in the phenotype

    c. Both alleles are expressed with dominant traits equally

    d. None of the above

4. Chargraff's rule states that:

    a. Concentrations of Adenine and Thymine are in close correlation

    b. Concentrations of Adenine and Cytosine are in close correlation

    c. Concentrations of Adenine and Guanine are in close correlation

    d. None of the above

5. DNA molecules consist of:

    a. 2 polynucleotide chains held together by bonds between complementary nitrogen bases

    b. 4 polynucleotide chains held together by bonds between complementary phosphorus bases

    c. 2 polynucleotide chains held together by bonds between complementary phosphorus bases

    d. None of the above

6. RNA differs from DNA for all of these reasons except:

a. It consists of 1 nucleotide chain instead of 2

b. Uses Uracil instead of Thymine

c. Uses ribose instead of deoxyribose

d. Adenine begins all RNA strands

7. Genetic code has many characteristics except:

a. The Genetic code is universal.

b. The Genetic code is unambiguous

c. The Genetic code is redundant

d. The genetic code is ambiguous

8. Which are the two correct types of mutations:

a. Germ Line, Somatic

b. Germ Line, Chromosomal linkage

c. Somatic, Chromosomal linkage

d. None

9. A point mutation:

a. Changes one nucleotide in the sequence

b. Delete one nucleotide

c. Add one nucleotide in the sequence

d. None of the above

10. What is the TATA box?

a. A regulatory element that is part of the promoter of most eucaryotic genes

b. A shoe box

c. The activation complex on DNA

11. What do Homeobox genes regulate?

a. Genes that regulate development

b. Genes that regulate hormones

c. Genes that regulate digestion

12. How many autosomes are there?

   a. 20

   b. 23

   c. 22

   d. 24

13. What is not a step in a Polymerase Chain Reaction?

   a. Denaturing

   b. Annealing

   c. Extension

   d. Formation

14. Recombinant DNA is:

   a. Pieces of DNA used to bring together other DNA strands to create new, unique strands of DNA

   b. Pieces of RNA used to bring together other RNA strands to create new, unique strands of DNA

   c. Pieces of RNA used to bring together other DNA strands to create new, unique strands of DNA

15. Relative dating measures:

   a. Which of two fossils is older

   b. How old the fossil is

   c. Where the fossil came from

   d. What the fossil is made of

16. What did Miller & Urey's experiment discover?

   a. Using sparks and molecular gases, Miller & Urey were able to create simple organic compounds.

   b. Volcanic eruptions caused simple organic compounds to form

   c. Organic compounds already occurred on earth

   d. None of the above

17. What does LUCA stand for?

    a. Last Universal Common Ancestor

    b. Last Unique Common Ancestor

    c. Likely Universal Common Ancestor

    d. None of these

18. The RNA world hypothesis states that:

    a. DNA coded for RNA, which started the first building blocks of life

    b. DNA was the first building block of life

    c. RNA was the first building block of life, not DNA, and DNA evolved later

    d. None of the above

58

Biology for the Rhetoric Stage

Unit 3 - Ecology, Eukaryotes, and Plant Life

Unit 3: Ecology, Eukaryotes, and Plant Life

Overview of Study

Notes

Week 1 Assignment Sheet - Principles of Ecology

Textbook Assignments

Reading
📖 *CK-12 Biology* Sections 11.1, 11.2, 11.3

Written
After you finish reading, answer questions #1-5 in section 11.1, questions #1-3 in section 11.2, and questions #1-3 in section 11.3. File your work in the reading section of your science notebook. Then, define the following terms in the glossary section of your science notebook:

- ☐ Abiotic factor
- ☐ Biotic factor
- ☐ Chemoautotroph
- ☐ Detritivore
- ☐ Photoautotroph
- ☐ Saprotroph
- ☐ Biogeochemical cycle
- ☐ Exchange pool
- ☐ Aphotic zone
- ☐ Intertidal zone
- ☐ Photic zone

Experiment - Ecology

Purpose
The purpose of this lab is to introduce students to population estimates and to population fluctuations related to changes in the environment.

Pre-Reading
⌇ Read the background and procedure sections for the "Ecology" lab in Late Nite Labs.

Procedure
✓ Do the lab entitled "Ecology" in Late Nite Labs.

Lab Notebook
☞ Write down on a sheet of paper or type out your notes in Late Nite Labs as you do the experiment. After you are done, print out your lab notes and add them to the lab section of your science notebook.

Lab Exam
↳ Complete the multiple choice section of the "Ecology" lab in Late Nite Labs. Submit the grade to your teacher.

Optional Hands-on
✂ Observe the ecosystem in which you live. You can do this from your backyard or from a local trail. Be sure to look for both abiotic and biotic factors. Afterwords, create a journal page detailing what you have observed.

Events in Science

Current Events
🕐 Find a current events article relating to the field of ecology and complete the article

summary sheet found on pg. 131 of the Appendix. Once you are done, add the sheet to the events section of your science notebook.

Historical Figures

🕐 Begin to research the life and work of Alexander von Humboldt, who is considered by many to be the father of modern ecology. You will have three weeks to complete your research. After that, you will have two weeks to prepare a two to three page paper on this scientist and his contributions to the field of biology.

Possible Schedules

Two Days a Week

Day 1	Day 2
❏ Read *CK-12 Biology* Sections 11.1 and 11.2.	❏ Read *CK-12 Biology* Section 11.3.
❏ Add the vocabulary to the glossary section of your science notebook.	❏ Answer the assigned questions in the reading section of your science notebook.
❏ Read the background and procedure sections for the week's lab.	❏ Do the "Ecology" lab in Late Nite Labs.
❏ Do the current events assignment and add the sheet to the events section of your science notebook.	❏ Record what you have done in the lab section of your science notebook and complete your lab exam for the week.

Five Days a Week

Day 1	Day 2	Day 3	Day 4	Day 5
❏ Read *CK-12 Biology* Sections 11.1 and 11.2. ❏ Add the vocabulary to the glossary section of your science notebook.	❏ Read *CK-12 Biology* Section 11.3. ❏ Answer the assigned questions in the reading section of your science notebook.	❏ Read the background and procedure sections for the week's lab.	❏ Do the "Ecology" lab in Late Nite Labs. ❏ Record what you have done in the lab section of your science notebook.	❏ Complete your lab exam for the week. ❏ Do the optional Hands-on Assignment.

Throughout the Week
❏ Choose one of the Events in Science assignments to do and add your work to the events section of your science notebook.

Week 2 Assignment Sheet - Communities and Populations, part 1

Textbook Assignments
Reading
📖 *CK-12 Biology* Sections 12.1, 12.2

Written
After you finish reading, answer questions #1-3 in section 12.1 and questions #1-5 in section 12.2. File your work in the reading section of your science notebook. Then, define the following terms in the glossary section of your science notebook:

- ☐ Commensalism
- ☐ Keystone species
- ☐ Mutualism
- ☐ Primary succession
- ☐ Secondary succession
- ☐ Carrying capacity
- ☐ Dispersal
- ☐ *r*-selected

Experiment - Your Community (Week 1)
Purpose
The purpose of this lab is to familiarize you with the flora and fauna in your local community.

Pre-Reading
〰 Read the assigned sections in the textbook before doing this lab.

Procedure
✓ This week, research the animals (fauna) and plants (flora) that live within a 20 mile radius of your home. Pick five of these animals to learn more about. For these animals, find out where they live (e.g., on the ground or in a tree), what they eat, and how they interact each other and their environment. You will have two weeks to complete this lab.

Lab Notebook
☞ Write down what you have learned from your research. After you are done, add the notes to the lab section of your science notebook.

Lab Exam
⚡ There is no exam for this lab.

Optional Hands-on
✂ Research the abiotic factors and resources that are found in your community.

Events in Science
Current Events
🕐 Find a current events article relating to the field of ecology and complete the article summary sheet found on pg. 131 of the Appendix. Once you are done, add the sheet to the events section of your science notebook.

Historical Figures

🕐 Continue to research the life and work of Alexander von Humboldt.

Possible Schedules

Two Days a Week

Day 1	Day 2
❏ Read *CK-12 Biology* Section 12.1. ❏ Add the vocabulary to the glossary section of your science notebook. ❏ Read the background and procedure sections for the week's lab. ❏ Do the current events assignment and add the sheet to the events section of your science notebook.	❏ Read *CK-12 Biology* Section 12.2. ❏ Answer the assigned questions in the reading section of your science notebook. ❏ Begin the "Your Community" lab. ❏ Record what you have done in the lab section of your science notebook.

Five Days a Week

Day 1	Day 2	Day 3	Day 4	Day 5
❏ Read *CK-12 Biology* Section 12.1. ❏ Add the vocabulary to the glossary section of your science notebook.	❏ Read *CK-12 Biology* Section 12.2. ❏ Answer the assigned questions in the reading section of your science notebook.	❏ Read the background and procedure sections for the week's lab.	❏ Begin the "Your Community" lab. ❏ Record what you have done in the lab section of your science notebook.	❏ Do the optional Hands-on Assignment.

Throughout the Week

❏ Choose one of the Events in Science assignments to do and add your work to the events section of your science notebook.

Week 3 Assignment Sheet - Communities and Populations, part 2

Textbook Assignments

Reading
📖 *CK-12 Biology* Sections 12.3, 12.4, 12.5

Written
After you finish reading, answer questions #1-3 in section 12.3, questions #1-4 in section 12.4, and questions #1-4 in section 12.5. File your work in the reading section of your science notebook. Then, define the following terms in the glossary section of your science notebook:

☐ Demographic transition   ☐ Algal bloom
☐ Sixth mass extinction   ☐ Ozone hole

Experiment - Your Community (Week 2)

Purpose
The purpose of this lab is to familiarize you with the flora and fauna in your local community.

Pre-Reading
〰 Re-read *CK-12 Biology* Section 11.1.

Procedure
✓ This week, draw a food web for your community using the five animals you chose from the previous week and several of the plants they feed on. Be sure to label them with their appropriate trophic levels (e.g., primary producer, primary consumer, and so on).

Lab Notebook
☞ After you are done your food web, add it to the lab section of your science notebook.

Lab Exam
🗲 There is no exam for this lab.

Optional Hands-on
✂ Draw another food web for your community.

Events in Science

Current Events
🕐 Find a current events article relating to the field of ecology and complete the article summary sheet found on pg. 131 of the Appendix. Once you are done, add the sheet to the events section of your science notebook.

Historical Figures
🕐 Continue to research the life and work of Alexander von Humboldt.

Possible Schedules

Two Days a Week

Day 1	Day 2
☐ Read *CK-12 Biology* Section 12.3 and 12.4.	☐ Read *CK-12 Biology* Section 12.5.
☐ Add the vocabulary to the glossary section of your science notebook.	☐ Answer the assigned questions in the reading section of your science notebook.
☐ Read the background and procedure sections for the week's lab.	☐ Finish the "Your Community" lab.
☐ Do the current events assignment and add the sheet to the events section of your science notebook.	☐ Record what you have done in the lab section of your science notebook.

Five Days a Week

Day 1	Day 2	Day 3	Day 4	Day 5
☐ Read *CK-12 Biology* Section 12.3 and 12.4. ☐ Add the vocabulary to the glossary section of your science notebook.	☐ Read *CK-12 Biology* Section 12.5. ☐ Answer the assigned questions in the reading section of your science notebook.	☐ Read the background and procedure sections for the week's lab.	☐ Finish the "Your Community" lab. ☐ Record what you have done in the lab section of your science notebook.	☐ Do the optional Hands-on Assignment.

Throughout the Week

☐ Choose one of the Events in Science assignments to do and add your work to the events section of your science notebook.

Week 4 Assignment Sheet - Microorganisms

Textbook Assignments

Reading
📖 *CK-12 Biology* Sections 13.1, 13.2

Written
After you finish reading, answer questions #1-5 in section 13.1 and questions #1-5 in section 13.2. File your work in the reading section of your science notebook. Then, define the following terms in the glossary section of your science notebook:

- ☐ Archaea
- ☐ Biofilm
- ☐ Cyanobacteria
- ☐ Extremophile
- ☐ Plasmid

- ☐ Vector
- ☐ Capsid
- ☐ Latency
- ☐ Vaccine
- ☐ Virion

Experiment - Bacteria

Purpose
The purpose of this lab is to stain bacteria to determine if they are gram+ or gram-.

Pre-Reading
〰 Read the background and procedure sections for the "Bacteria" lab in Late Nite Labs.

Procedure
✓ Do the lab entitled "Bacteria" in Late Nite Labs.

Lab Notebook
☞ Write down on a sheet of paper or type out your notes in Late Nite Labs as you do the experiment. After you are done, print out your lab notes and add them to the lab section of your science notebook.

Lab Exam
↯ Complete the multiple choice section of the "Bacteria" lab in Late Nite Labs. Submit the grade to your teacher.

Optional Hands-on
✂ Take sample swabs from different places around your home. Then, plate these samples and watch the bacteria grow.

Events in Science

Current Events
🕑 Find a current events article relating to the field of microbiology and complete the article summary sheet found on pg. 131 of the Appendix. Once you are done, add the sheet to the events section of your science notebook.

Historical Figures

🕐 Begin to work on your paper on the life and work of Alexander von Humboldt. This week, aim to complete your outline and rough draft. See pg. 118 in the Appendix for more directions. You will have three weeks to complete this paper.

Possible Schedules

Two Days a Week

Day 1	Day 2
❏ Read *CK-12 Biology* Section 13.1.	❏ Read *CK-12 Biology* Section 13.2.
❏ Add the vocabulary to the glossary section of your science notebook.	❏ Answer the assigned questions in the reading section of your science notebook.
❏ Read the background and procedure sections for the week's lab.	❏ Do the "Bacteria" lab in Late Nite Labs.
❏ Do the current events assignment and add the sheet to the events section of your science notebook.	❏ Record what you have done in the lab section of your science notebook and complete your lab exam for the week.

Five Days a Week

Day 1	Day 2	Day 3	Day 4	Day 5
❏ Read *CK-12 Biology* Section 13.1.	❏ Read *CK-12 Biology* Section 13.2.	❏ Read the background and procedure sections for the week's lab.	❏ Do the "Bacteria" lab in Late Nite Labs.	❏ Complete your lab exam for the week.
❏ Add the vocabulary to the glossary section of your science notebook.	❏ Answer the assigned questions in the reading section of your science notebook.		❏ Record what you have done in the lab section of your science notebook.	❏ Do the optional Hands-on Assignment.

Throughout the Week

❏ Choose one of the Events in Science assignments to do and add your work to the events section of your science notebook.

70

Week 5 Assignment Sheet - Eukaryotes, part 1

Textbook Assignments
Reading
📖 *CK-12 Biology* Sections 14.1, 14.2, 14.3
Written
After you finish reading, answer questions #1-3 in section 14.1, questions #1-3 in section 14.2, and questions #3, 4 in section 14.3. File your work in the reading section of your science notebook. Then, define the following terms in the glossary section of your science notebook:

- Cilia
- Motility
- Protist
- Pseudopod
- Amoeboid
- Flagellate
- Protozoa

- Slime mold
- Sporozoa
- Budding
- Chitin
- Hyphae
- Mycelium
- Zygospore

Experiment - Investigating Fungi
Purpose
The purpose of this lab is to examine examples of kingdom fungi with emphasis on variations in structure and reproduction.
Pre-Reading
Read the background and procedure sections for the "Investigating Fungi" lab in Late Nite Labs.
Procedure
✓ Do the lab entitled "Investigating Fungi" in Late Nite Labs.
Lab Notebook
☞ Write down on a sheet of paper or type out your notes in Late Nite Labs as you do the experiment. After you are done, print out your lab notes and add them to the lab section of your science notebook.
Lab Exam
🖊 Complete the multiple choice section of the "Investigating Fungi" lab in Late Nite Labs. Submit the grade to your teacher.
Optional Hands-on
✂ Look for a mushroom outside. Then, with gloves on, remove the mushroom for observation and dig below it to look for mycelium to observe. Use a magnifying glass or hand-held microscope (a.k.a. jeweler's scope) to look closer of the structures of a fungus.

Events in Science

Current Events

⏰ Find a current events article relating to the field of microbiology and complete the article summary sheet found on pg. 131 of the Appendix. Once you are done, add the sheet to the events section of your science notebook.

Historical Figures

⏰ Continue to work on your paper on the life and work of Alexander von Humboldt. This week, aim to complete your final draft. See pg. 118 in the Appendix for more directions.

Possible Schedules

Two Days a Week

Day 1	Day 2
❏ Read *CK-12 Biology* Section 14.1 and 14.2.	❏ Read *CK-12 Biology* Section 14.3.
❏ Add the vocabulary to the glossary section of your science notebook.	❏ Answer the assigned questions in the reading section of your science notebook.
❏ Read the background and procedure sections for the week's lab.	❏ Do the "Investigating Fungi" lab in Late Nite Labs.
❏ Do the current events assignment and add the sheet to the events section of your science notebook.	❏ Record what you have done in the lab section of your science notebook and complete your lab exam for the week.

Five Days a Week

Day 1	Day 2	Day 3	Day 4	Day 5
❏ Read *CK-12 Biology* Section 14.1 and 14.2. ❏ Add the vocabulary to the glossary section of your science notebook.	❏ Read *CK-12 Biology* Section 14.3. ❏ Answer the assigned questions in the reading section of your science notebook.	❏ Read the background and procedure sections for the week's lab.	❏ Do the "Investigating Fungi" lab in Late Nite Labs. ❏ Record what you have done in the lab section of your science notebook.	❏ Complete your lab exam for the week. ❏ Do the optional Hands-on Assignment.

Throughout the Week
❏ Choose one of the Events in Science assignments to do and add your work to the events section of your science notebook.

Week 6 Assignment Sheet - Eukaryotes, part 2

Textbook Assignments

Reading
📖 *CK-12 Biology* Sections 14. 4, 14.5

Written
After you finish reading, answer questions #1-4 in section 14.4 and questions #1-4 in 14.5. File your work in the reading section of your science notebook. Then, define the following terms in the glossary section of your science notebook:

- [ ] Lichen
- [ ] Mycorrhiza
- [ ] Candidiasis
- [ ] Giardiasis
- [ ] Malaria
- [ ] Ringworm

Experiment - Protists

Purpose
The purpose of this lab is to learn about eukaryotic super groups through examination of representative members.

Pre-Reading
✍ Read the background and procedure sections for the "Protists" lab in Late Nite Labs.

Procedure
✓ Do the lab entitled "Protists" in Late Nite Labs.

Lab Notebook
☞ Write down on a sheet of paper or type out your notes in Late Nite Labs as you do the experiment. After you are done, print out your lab notes and add them to the lab section of your science notebook.

Lab Exam
↳ Complete the multiple choice section of the "Protists" lab in Late Nite Labs. Submit the grade to your teacher.

Optional Hands-on
✂ Study the different types of lichens. Directions for this project can be found here: http://elementalblogging.com/homeschool-science-lichens/.

Events in Science

Current Events
🕐 Find a current events article relating to the field of microbiology and complete the article summary sheet found on pg. 131 of the Appendix. Once you are done, add the sheet to the events section of your science notebook.

Historical Figures
🕐 Begin to research the life and work of Carl Linnaeus, who is considered by many to

be the father of modern biological classification systems. You will have two weeks to complete your research. After that, you will have two weeks to prepare a two to three page paper on this scientist and his contributions to the field of biology.

Possible Schedules

Two Days a Week

Day 1	Day 2
❑ Read *CK-12 Biology* Section 14.4.	❑ Read *CK-12 Biology* Section 14.5.
❑ Add the vocabulary to the glossary section of your science notebook.	❑ Answer the assigned questions in the reading section of your science notebook.
❑ Read the background and procedure sections for the week's lab.	❑ Do the "Protists" lab in Late Nite Labs.
❑ Do the current events assignment and add the sheet to the events section of your science notebook.	❑ Record what you have done in the lab section of your science notebook and complete your lab exam for the week.

Five Days a Week

Day 1	Day 2	Day 3	Day 4	Day 5
❑ Read *CK-12 Biology* Section 14.4. ❑ Add the vocabulary to the glossary section of your science notebook.	❑ Read *CK-12 Biology* Section 14.5. ❑ Answer the assigned questions in the reading section of your science notebook.	❑ Read the background and procedure sections for the week's lab.	❑ Do the "Protists" lab in Late Nite Labs. ❑ Record what you have done in the lab section of your science notebook.	❑ Complete your lab exam for the week. ❑ Do the optional Hands-on Assignment.

Throughout the Week

❑ Choose one of the Events in Science assignments to do and add your work to the events section of your science notebook.

Week 7 Assignment Sheet - Plant Evolution and Classification

Textbook Assignments

Reading
    📖 *CK-12 Biology* Sections 15.1, 15.2

Written
After you finish reading, answer questions #1-5 in section 15.1 and questions #1-4 in section 15.2. File your work in the reading section of your science notebook. Then, define the following terms in the glossary section of your science notebook:

- ☐ Gametophyte
- ☐ Lignin
- ☐ Rhizoid
- ☐ Sporophyte
- ☐ Bryophyte
- ☐ Phloem
- ☐ Sepal
- ☐ Spermatophyte
- ☐ Tracheophyte
- ☐ Xylem

Experiment - Plant Structure and Function

Purpose
The purpose of this lab is to examine examples of kingdom plantae, with emphasis on characterizing plants by the presence and arrangement of vascular tissue.

Pre-Reading
    ☞ Read the background and procedure sections for the "Plant Structure and Function" lab in Late Nite Labs.

Procedure
    ✓ Do the lab entitled "Plant Structure and Function" in Late Nite Labs.

Lab Notebook
    ☞ Write down on a sheet of paper or type out your notes in Late Nite Labs as you do the experiment. After you are done, print out your lab notes and add them to the lab section of your science notebook.

Lab Exam
    ↳ Complete the multiple choice section of the "Plant Structure and Function" lab in Late Nite Labs. Submit the grade to your teacher.

Optional Hands-on
    ✄ Dissect a flower and identify the various parts. Directions for this project can be found here: http://elementalscience.com/blogs/science-activities/94044099-how-to-dissect-a-flower.

Events in Science

Current Events
    🕐 Find a current events article relating to the field of botany and complete the article

summary sheet found on pg. 131 of the Appendix. Once you are done, add the sheet to the events section of your science notebook.

Historical Figures

🕐 Continue to research the life and work of Carl Linnaeus.

Possible Schedules

Two Days a Week

Day 1	Day 2
❑ Read *CK-12 Biology* Section 15.1.	❑ Read *CK-12 Biology* Section 15.2.
❑ Add the vocabulary to the glossary section of your science notebook.	❑ Answer the assigned questions in the reading section of your science notebook.
❑ Read the background and procedure sections for the week's lab.	❑ Do the "Plant Structure and Function" lab in Late Nite Labs.
❑ Do the current events assignment and add the sheet to the events section of your science notebook.	❑ Record what you have done in the lab section of your science notebook and complete your lab exam for the week.

Five Days a Week

Day 1	Day 2	Day 3	Day 4	Day 5
❑ Read *CK-12 Biology* Section 15.1. ❑ Add the vocabulary to the glossary section of your science notebook.	❑ Read *CK-12 Biology* Section 15.2. ❑ Answer the assigned questions in the reading section of your science notebook.	❑ Read the background and procedure sections for the week's lab.	❑ Do the "Plant Structure and Function" lab in Late Nite Labs. ❑ Record what you have done in the lab section of your science notebook.	❑ Complete your lab exam for the week. ❑ Do the optional Hands-on Assignment.

Throughout the Week
❑ Choose one of the Events in Science assignments to do and add your work to the events section of your science notebook.

Week 8 Assignment Sheet - Plant Biology, part 1

Textbook Assignments
Reading
📖 *CK-12 Biology* Sections 16.1, 16.2
Written
After you finish reading, answer questions #1-4 in section 16.1 and questions #1-5 in section 16.2. File your work in the reading section of your science notebook. Then, define the following terms in the glossary section of your science notebook:
- ☐ Cuticle
- ☐ Dermal tissue
- ☐ Ground tissue
- ☐ Meristem
- ☐ Mesophyll
- ☐ Stomata
- ☐ Taproot

Experiment - Plant Reproduction
Purpose
The purpose of this lab is to observe seed plant reproduction.
Pre-Reading
☞ Read the background and procedure sections for the "Plant Reproduction" lab in Late Nite Labs.
Procedure
✓ Do the lab entitled "Plant Reproduction" in Late Nite Labs.
Lab Notebook
☞ Write down on a sheet of paper or type out your notes in Late Nite Labs as you do the experiment. After you are done, print out your lab notes and add them to the lab section of your science notebook.
Lab Exam
↯ Complete the multiple choice section of the "Plant Reproduction" lab in Late Nite Labs. Submit the grade to your teacher.
Optional Hands-on
✂ Sprout an onion by suspending it in a glass of water. Once the roots have appeared, observe the root cap, meristem, and root hairs. If you have a microscope, place a cross-section of the root tip on a slide, stain it, and examine it under the microscope.

Events in Science
Current Events
🕓 Find a current events article relating to the field of botany and complete the article summary sheet found on pg. 131 of the Appendix. Once you are done, add the sheet to the events section of your science notebook.

Historical Figures

🕐 Begin to work on your paper on the life and work of Carl Linnaeus. This week, aim to complete your outline and rough draft. See pg. 118 in the Appendix for more directions. You will have two weeks to complete this paper.

Possible Schedules

Two Days a Week

Day 1	Day 2
❑ Read *CK-12 Biology* Section 16.1.	❑ Read *CK-12 Biology* Section 16.2.
❑ Add the vocabulary to the glossary section of your science notebook.	❑ Answer the assigned questions in the reading section of your science notebook.
❑ Read the background and procedure sections for the week's lab.	❑ Do the "Plant Reproduction" lab in Late Nite Labs.
❑ Do the current events assignment and add the sheet to the events section of your science notebook.	❑ Record what you have done in the lab section of your science notebook and complete your lab exam for the week.

Five Days a Week

Day 1	Day 2	Day 3	Day 4	Day 5
❑ Read *CK-12 Biology* Section 16.1. ❑ Add the vocabulary to the glossary section of your science notebook.	❑ Read *CK-12 Biology* Section 16.2. ❑ Answer the assigned questions in the reading section of your science notebook.	❑ Read the background and procedure sections for the week's lab.	❑ Do the "Plant Reproduction" lab in Late Nite Labs. ❑ Record what you have done in the lab section of your science notebook.	❑ Complete your lab exam for the week. ❑ Do the optional Hands-on Assignment.

Throughout the Week
❑ Choose one of the Events in Science assignments to do and add your work to the events section of your science notebook.

Week 9 Assignment Sheet - Plant Biology, part 2

Textbook Assignments

Reading

📖 *CK-12 Biology* Sections 16.3, 16.4

Written

After you finish reading, answer questions #1-5 in section 16.3 and questions #1-4,7 in section 16.4. File your work in the reading section of your science notebook. Then, define the following terms in the glossary section of your science notebook:

- ☐ Antheridia
- ☐ Archegonia
- ☐ Sporangium
- ☐ Epiphyte
- ☐ Tropism
- ☐ Xerophyte

Experiment - Full Lab Report

Lab Notebook

☞ This week, choose one of your previous labs and begin to write a full lab report. See pg. 113 for directions on how to write a full lab report. You will have two weeks to complete your write-up.

Optional Hands-on

✂ Make a terrarium so that you can observe the cycle of growth that mosses go through. You will need a large clear jar, aquarium pebbles or other small rocks, a bit of activated charcoal (to prevent bacterial growth), potting soil, and moss. Start by adding the pebbles, followed by the charcoal and soil. Then, place your moss on top of the soil near the edge of the jar and press down gently. Add a bit of water to moisten the soil, put the lid on the jar, and set it in a sunny place. Over the next few weeks observe the moss, looking for the rhizoids and sporophytes to develop.

Events in Science

Current Events

🕐 Find a current events article relating to the field of botany and complete the article summary sheet found on pg. 131 of the Appendix. Once you are done, add the sheet to the events section of your science notebook.

Historical Figures

🕐 Continue to work on your paper on the life and work of Carl Linnaeus. This week, aim to complete your final draft. See pg. 118 in the Appendix for more directions.

Possible Schedules

Two Days a Week

Day 1	Day 2
❑ Read *CK-12 Biology* Section 16.3 and 16.4. ❑ Add the vocabulary to the glossary section of your science notebook. ❑ Answer the assigned questions in the reading section of your science notebook.	❑ Work on the full Lab Report. ❑ Do the current events assignment and add the sheet to the events section of your science notebook.

Five Days a Week

Day 1	Day 2	Day 3	Day 4	Day 5
❑ Read *CK-12 Biology* Section 16.3. ❑ Add the vocabulary to the glossary section of your science notebook.	❑ Read *CK-12 Biology* Section 16.3. ❑ Answer the assigned questions in the reading section of your science notebook.	❑ Work on the full Lab Report.	❑ Work on the full Lab Report.	❑ Do the optional Hands-on Assignment.

Throughout the Week

❑ Choose one of the Events in Science assignments to do and add your work to the events section of your science notebook.

Unit 3 Test

1. A niche is:

   a. Another name for a fox den.

   b. The physical environment the species lives in

   c. Ways a species interact with the abiotic and biotic factors of their enviornment

   d. A place where animals live.

2. The definition of a saphrotroph is:

   a. They consume the soft tissue of dead animals

   b. They consume the detritus of other species

   c. Feed on the remaining waste of detritovores and scavengers

3. Water changes to a gas in three ways. Which way below is not a correct answer?

   a. Sublimation

   b. Evaporation

   c. Transpiration

   d. Liquidation

4. Which type below is not a pattern of population distribution?

   a. Clumped

   b. Random

   c. Uniform

   d. Structured

5. When did major changes in human population begin to occur on earth?

   a. 1900s

   b. 1800s

   c. 1700s

   d. 1600s

6. What is biodiversity?

   a. Variety of life and its processes, including genetic differences, life, and ecosystems

   b. Number of each similar species in a group

   c. Quantity of each species in a given group

   d. None of the above

7. Ozone on our planet is:

    a. Harmful in the upper atmosphere, helpful in the lower atmosphere

    b. Helpful in the upper atmosphere, helpful in the lower atmosphere

    c. Helpful in the upper atmosphere, harmful in the lower atmosphere

    d. None of the above

8. Why are cyanobacteria so helpful to life on earth?

    a. They produce cyanide, a helpful precursor in reactions

    b. The produce food through photosynthesis and release oxygen

    c. The help replicate and reproduce DNA in other bacteria

    d. None of the above

9. The three most common shapes of prokaryotes are as follows:

    a. Rod, sphere, square

    b. Helix, sphere, rod

    c. Oval, sphere, rod

    d. None of the above

10. All of the below are hypothesises that scientists have made for the arise of viruses, except:

    a. Runaway pieces of nucleic acid from living cells

    b. Parasitic cells inside other larger host cells

    c. Runaway RNA strands that were exported from the cell

11. Protists are not:

    a. Animals, Plants, or Fungi

    b. Prokaryotes

    c. Complex Eukaryotes

12. Most protists have motility; they move using any of these, except:

    a. Cilia

    b. Pseudopod

    c. Flagella

    d. Tubercle

13. Plant-like protists are called:

   a. Slime molds

   b. Ameboid

   c. Algae

   d. Sporozoa

14. All are considered algae except:

   a. Red

   b. Green

   c. Euglenoid

   d. Flagellates

15. Fungi grows as threadlike elements called:

   a. Mycelia

   b. Hyphae

   c. Chitin

   d. None of the above

16. A mycorrhiza is:

   a. An advesarial relationship between a fungus and a plant.

   b. A mutualistic relationship between algae and a plant.

   c. A mutualistic relationship between a fungus and a plant.

   d. None of the above.

17. Plants are important to humans for all of the following reasons except:

   a. Plants supply food to almost all terrestrial animals, including humans

   b. Plants maintain the earth's oxygen

   c. Plants recycle matter in biochemical processes

   d. Plants release CO_2 and use O_2

18. Which chemical compound adds rigidity and strength to plants?

   a. Pectin

   b. Lignin

   c. Chromatin

   d. None of the above

19. Gymnosperms produce seeds in:

    a. Cones

    b. Shells

    c. Leaves

    d. Roots

20. Plants use the following root structures, except:

    a. Tap roots

    b. Fibrous roots

    c. Filamentous roots

21. In seed plants, the gametophyte generation takes place in:

    a. A rhizome

    b. A cone or flower

    c. The leaf of the plant

    d. None of the above

Biology for the Rhetoric Stage

Unit 4 - Animals and the Human Body

Unit 4: Animals and the Human Body

Overview of Study

Notes

Week 1 Assignment Sheet - Introduction to Animals

Textbook Assignments

Reading
📖 *CK-12 Biology* Sections 17.1, 17.2

Written
After you finish reading, answer questions #1-4 in section 17.1 and questions #1-6 in section 17.2. File your work in the reading section of your science notebook. Then, define the following terms in the glossary section of your science notebook:

- ☐ Amniote
- ☐ Notochord
- ☐ Bilateral symmetry
- ☐ Cephalization
- ☐ Coelom
- ☐ Endoderm
- ☐ Mesoderm
- ☐ Pseudocoelom
- ☐ Radial symmetry
- ☐ Segmentation

Experiment - Full Lab Report

Lab Notebook
☞ This week, finish writing the full lab report you began at the end of unit 3. See pg. 113 for directions on how to write a full lab report. Add your completed write-up to your lab notebook.

Optional Hands-on
✂ This week, dissect a starfish using a kit that you can purchase from Carolina Biological, Rainbow Resources, or Home Science Tools.

Events in Science

Current Events
🕐 Find a current events article relating to the field of zoology and complete the article summary sheet found on pg. 131 of the Appendix. Once you are done, add the sheet to the events section of your science notebook.

Historical Figures
🕐 Begin to research the life and work of Charles Henry Turner, who changed the way we think about insects. You will have two weeks to complete your research. After that, you will have two weeks to prepare a two to three page paper on this scientist and his contributions to the field of biology.

Possible Schedules

Two Days a Week

Day 1	Day 2
❏ Read *CK-12 Biology* Sections 17.1. ❏ Add the vocabulary to the glossary section of your science notebook. ❏ Answer the assigned questions in the reading section of your science notebook.	❏ Read *CK-12 Biology* Sections 17.2. ❏ Finish the full Lab Report. ❏ Do the current events assignment and add the sheet to the events section of your science notebook.

Five Days a Week

Day 1	Day 2	Day 3	Day 4	Day 5
❏ Read *CK-12 Biology* Sections 17.1. ❏ Add the vocabulary to the glossary section of your science notebook.	❏ Read *CK-12 Biology* Sections 17.2. ❏ Answer the assigned questions in the reading section of your science notebook.	❏ Work on the full Lab Report.	❏ Finish the full Lab Report.	❏ Do the optional Hands-on Assignment.

Throughout the Week
❏ Choose one of the Events in Science assignments to do and add your work to the events section of your science notebook.

Week 2 Assignment Sheet - Invertebrates

Textbook Assignments

Reading
📖 *CK-12 Biology* Sections 18.1, 18.2, 18.3, 18.4

Written
After you finish reading, answer questions #1-4 in section 18.1, questions #1-4 in section 18.2, questions #1-4 in section 18.3, and questions #1-4 in section 18.4. File your work in the reading section of your science notebook. Then, define the following terms in the glossary section of your science notebook:

- [ ] Cnidarian
- [ ] Medusa
- [ ] Platyhelminthes
- [ ] Sessile
- [ ] Annelida

- [ ] Regeneration
- [ ] Trilobite
- [ ] Chordates
- [ ] Echinoderms
- [ ] Tunicates

Experiment - Earthworm

Purpose
The purpose of this lab is to examine samples of kingdom Animalia through examination of an earthworm.

Pre-Reading
🖎 Read the background and procedure sections for the "Earthworm" lab in Late Nite Labs.

Procedure
✓ Do the lab entitled "Earthworm" in Late Nite Labs.

Lab Notebook
☞ Write down on a sheet of paper or type out your notes in Late Nite Labs as you do the experiment. After you are done, print out your lab notes and add them to the lab section of your science notebook.

Lab Exam
⚡ Complete the multiple choice section of the "Earthworm" lab in Late Nite Labs. Submit the grade to your teacher.

Optional Hands-on
✂ Create your own worm farm. You can purchase a pre-made one or make your own using the following directions: http://modernfarmer.com/2013/05/how-to-build-a-worm-farm/.

Events in Science

Current Events
🕐 Find a current events article relating to the field of zoology and complete the article

summary sheet found on pg. 131 of the Appendix. Once you are done, add the sheet to the events section of your science notebook.

Historical Figures
🕐 Continue to research the life and work of Charles Henry Turner.

Possible Schedules

Two Days a Week

Day 1	Day 2
☐ Read *CK-12 Biology* Section 18.1 and 18.2. ☐ Add the vocabulary to the glossary section of your science notebook. ☐ Read the background and procedure sections for the week's lab. ☐ Do the current events assignment and add the sheet to the events section of your science notebook.	☐ Read *CK-12 Biology* Section 18.3 and 18.4. ☐ Answer the assigned questions in the reading section of your science notebook. ☐ Do the "Earthworm" lab in Late Nite Labs. ☐ Record what you have done in the lab section of your science notebook and complete your lab exam for the week.

Five Days a Week

Day 1	Day 2	Day 3	Day 4	Day 5
☐ Read *CK-12 Biology* Section 18.1 and 18.2. ☐ Add the vocabulary to the glossary section of your science notebook.	☐ Read *CK-12 Biology* Section 18.3 and 18.4. ☐ Answer the assigned questions in the reading section of your science notebook.	☐ Read the background and procedure sections for the week's lab.	☐ Do the "Earthworm" lab in Late Nite Labs. ☐ Record what you have done in the lab section of your science notebook.	☐ Complete your lab exam for the week. ☐ Do the optional Hands-on Assignment.

Throughout the Week

☐ Choose one of the Events in Science assignments to do and add your work to the events section of your science notebook.

Week 3 Assignment Sheet - Fish to Birds

Textbook Assignments
Reading
📖 *CK-12 Biology* Sections 19.1, 19.2, 19.3, 19.4, 19.5

Written
After you finish reading, answer questions #1-4 in section 19.1, questions #1,3,5 in section 19.2, questions #1,3,5 in section 19.3, questions #1-4 in section 19.4, and questions #1-4 in section 19.5. File your work in the reading section of your science notebook. Then, define the following terms in the glossary section of your science notebook:

- [ ] Ectothermic
- [ ] Endothermic
- [ ] Ovipary
- [ ] Ovovivipary
- [ ] Vivipary
- [ ] Spawning
- [ ] Tetrapod
- [ ] Incubation

Experiment - Biological Molecules
Purpose
The purpose of this lab is to describe the role of macromolecules in living organisms and their food sources.

Pre-Reading
  Read the background and procedure sections for the "Biological Molecules" lab in Late Nite Labs.

Procedure
✓ Do the lab entitled "Biological Molecules" in Late Nite Labs.

Lab Notebook
☞ Write down on a sheet of paper or type out your notes in Late Nite Labs as you do the experiment. After you are done, print out your lab notes and add them to the lab section of your science notebook.

Lab Exam
↬ Complete the multiple choice section of the "Biological Molecules" lab in Late Nite Labs. Submit the grade to your teacher.

Optional Hands-on
✂ This week, dissect a perch using a kit that you can purchase from Carolina Biological, Rainbow Resources, or Home Science Tools.

Events in Science
Current Events
🕐 Find a current events article relating to the field of zoology and complete the article summary sheet found on pg. 131 of the Appendix. Once you are done, add the sheet to

the events section of your science notebook.

Historical Figures

☺ Begin to work on your paper on the life and work of Charles Henry Turner. This week, aim to complete your outline and rough draft. See pg. 118 in the Appendix for more directions. You will have three weeks to complete this paper.

Possible Schedules

Two Days a Week

Day 1	Day 2
❏ Read *CK-12 Biology* Section 19.1 to 19.3. ❏ Add the vocabulary to the glossary section of your science notebook. ❏ Read the background and procedure sections for the week's lab. ❏ Do the current events assignment and add the sheet to the events section of your science notebook.	❏ Read *CK-12 Biology* Section 19.4 and 19.5. ❏ Answer the assigned questions in the reading section of your science notebook. ❏ Do the "Biological Molecules" lab in Late Nite Labs. ❏ Record what you have done in the lab section of your science notebook and complete your lab exam for the week.

Five Days a Week

Day 1	Day 2	Day 3	Day 4	Day 5
❏ Read *CK-12 Biology* Section 19.1 to 19.3. ❏ Add the vocabulary to the glossary section of your science notebook.	❏ Read *CK-12 Biology* Section 19.4 and 19.5. ❏ Answer the assigned questions in the reading section of your science notebook.	❏ Read the background and procedure sections for the week's lab.	❏ Do the "Biological Molecules" lab in Late Nite Labs. ❏ Record what you have done in the lab section of your science notebook.	❏ Complete your lab exam for the week. ❏ Do the optional Hands-on Assignment.

Throughout the Week

❏ Choose one of the Events in Science assignments to do and add your work to the events section of your science notebook.

Week 4 Assignment Sheet - Mammals

Textbook Assignments

Reading

📖 *CK-12 Biology* Sections 20.1, 20.2, 20.4

Written

After you finish reading, answer questions #1-4 in section 20.1, questions #1,3,5 in section 20.2, and questions #1-5 in section 20.4. File your work in the reading section of your science notebook. Then, define the following terms in the glossary section of your science notebook:

- ☐ Arboreal
- ☐ Cerebrum
- ☐ Neocortex
- ☐ Placenta
- ☐ Therian mammal
- ☐ Circadian rhythm
- ☐ Ethology
- ☐ Instinct

Experiment - Mammalian Tissue

Purpose

The purpose of this lab is to explain the organizational structure of organisms (cells, tissues, organs, and organ systems).

Pre-Reading

〰 Read the background and procedure sections for the "Mammalian Tissue" lab in Late Nite Labs.

Procedure

✓ Do the lab entitled "Mammalian Tissue" in Late Nite Labs.

Lab Notebook

☞ Write down on a sheet of paper or type out your notes in Late Nite Labs as you do the experiment. After you are done, print out your lab notes and add them to the lab section of your science notebook.

Lab Exam

🗲 Complete the multiple choice section of the "Mammalian Tissue" lab in Late Nite Labs. Submit the grade to your teacher.

Optional Hands-on

✂ Observe mammalian behavior. You can do this by observing the behavior of your pet cat or dog, or by heading out to a local park to observe human behavior.

Events in Science

Current Events

🕐 Find a current events article relating to the field of zoology and complete the article summary sheet found on pg. 131 of the Appendix. Once you are done, add the sheet to

the events section of your science notebook.

Historical Figures

⊕ Continue to work on your paper on the life and work of Charles Henry Turner. This week, aim to complete your final draft. See pg. 118 in the Appendix for more directions.

Possible Schedules

Two Days a Week

Day 1	Day 2
❑ Read *CK-12 Biology* Section 20.1 and 20.2.	❑ Read *CK-12 Biology* Section 20.4.
❑ Add the vocabulary to the glossary section of your science notebook.	❑ Answer the assigned questions in the reading section of your science notebook.
❑ Read the background and procedure sections for the week's lab.	❑ Do the "Mammalian Tissue" lab in Late Nite Labs.
❑ Do the current events assignment and add the sheet to the events section of your science notebook.	❑ Record what you have done in the lab section of your science notebook and complete your lab exam for the week.

Five Days a Week

Day 1	Day 2	Day 3	Day 4	Day 5
❑ Read *CK-12 Biology* Section 20.1 and 20.2. ❑ Add the vocabulary to the glossary section of your science notebook.	❑ Read *CK-12 Biology* Section 20.4. ❑ Answer the assigned questions in the reading section of your science notebook.	❑ Read the background and procedure sections for the week's lab.	❑ Do the "Mammalian Tissue" lab in Late Nite Labs. ❑ Record what you have done in the lab section of your science notebook.	❑ Complete your lab exam for the week. ❑ Do the optional Hands-on Assignment.

Throughout the Week

❑ Choose one of the Events in Science assignments to do and add your work to the events section of your science notebook.

Week 5 Assignment Sheet - Introduction to the Human Body

Textbook Assignments

Reading
📖 *CK-12 Biology* Sections 21.1, 21.2, 21.3, 21.4

Written
After you finish reading, answer questions #1-4 in section 20.1, questions #1-4 in section 21.2, questions #1-4 in section 21.3, and questions #1-5 in section 21.4. File your work in the reading section of your science notebook. Then, define the following terms in the glossary section of your science notebook:

- ☐ Connective tissue
- ☐ Epithelial tissue
- ☐ Bone matrix
- ☐ Osteoblast
- ☐ Osteoclast
- ☐ Osteocyte
- ☐ Periosteum
- ☐ Sliding filament theory
- ☐ Melanin
- ☐ Sebaceous gland

Experiment - Enzymes

Purpose
The purpose of this lab is to explore enzymatic activity.

Pre-Reading
✍ Read the background and procedure sections for the "Enzymes" lab in Late Nite Labs.

Procedure
✓ Do the lab entitled "Enzymes" in Late Nite Labs.

Lab Notebook
☞ Write down on a sheet of paper or type out your notes in Late Nite Labs as you do the experiment. After you are done, print out your lab notes and add them to the lab section of your science notebook.

Lab Exam
🗲 Complete the multiple choice section of the "Enzymes" lab in Late Nite Labs. Submit the grade to your teacher.

Optional Hands-on
✂ Make a model of the spine using a pool noodle, washers, hair ties, and nylon rope. Directions can be found in the following video: https://www.youtube.com/watch?v=Z6u0xI1JIP8.

Events in Science

Current Events
🕐 Find a current events article relating to the field of anatomy and complete the article summary sheet found on pg. 131 of the Appendix. Once you are done, add the sheet to

the events section of your science notebook.

Historical Figures

🕐 Begin to research the life and work of James Watson, who along with Francis Crick discovered the structure of DNA. You will have three weeks to complete your research. After that, you will have two weeks to prepare a two to three page paper on this scientist and his contributions to the field of biology.

Possible Schedules

Two Days a Week

Day 1	Day 2
❏ Read *CK-12 Biology* Section 21.1 and 21.2. ❏ Add the vocabulary to the glossary section of your science notebook. ❏ Read the background and procedure sections for the week's lab. ❏ Do the current events assignment and add the sheet to the events section of your science notebook.	❏ Read *CK-12 Biology* Section 21.3 and 21.4. ❏ Answer the assigned questions in the reading section of your science notebook. ❏ Do the "Enzymes" lab in Late Nite Labs. ❏ Record what you have done in the lab section of your science notebook and complete your lab exam for the week.

Five Days a Week

Day 1	Day 2	Day 3	Day 4	Day 5
❏ Read *CK-12 Biology* Section 21.1 and 21.2. ❏ Add the vocabulary to the glossary section of your science notebook.	❏ Read *CK-12 Biology* Section 21.3 and 21.4. ❏ Answer the assigned questions in the reading section of your science notebook.	❏ Read the background and procedure sections for the week's lab.	❏ Do the "Enzymes" lab in Late Nite Labs. ❏ Record what you have done in the lab section of your science notebook.	❏ Complete your lab exam for the week. ❏ Do the optional Hands-on Assignment.
Throughout the Week				
❏ Choose one of the Events in Science assignments to do and add your work to the events section of your science notebook.				

Week 6 Assignment Sheet - Nervous and Endocrine Systems

Textbook Assignments

Reading
📖 *CK-12 Biology* Sections 22.1, 22.2

Written
After you finish reading, answer questions #1,3,5,7 in section 22.1 and questions #1-4 in section 22.2. File your work in the reading section of your science notebook. Then, define the following terms in the glossary section of your science notebook:

☐ Autonomic Nervous System (ANS) ☐ Myelin sheath
☐ Central Nervous System (CNS) ☐ Neurotransmitter
☐ Dendrite ☐ Synapse
☐ Interneuron ☐ Target cell

Experiment - Quantitative Analysis of Enzymatic Activity

Purpose
The purpose of this lab is to describe the function of enzymes and explore the effects of environmental factors on enzymes.

Pre-Reading
෴ Read the background and procedure sections for the "Quantitative Analysis of Enzymatic Activity" lab in Late Nite Labs.

Procedure
✓ Do the lab entitled "Quantitative Analysis of Enzymatic Activity" in Late Nite Labs.

Lab Notebook
☞ Write down on a sheet of paper or type out your notes in Late Nite Labs as you do the experiment. After you are done, print out your lab notes and add them to the lab section of your science notebook.

Lab Exam
🗲 Complete the multiple choice section of the "Quantitative Analysis of Enzymatic Activity" lab in Late Nite Labs. Submit the grade to your teacher.

Optional Hands-on
✄ Make a model of the a neuron using pom-poms, pipe cleaners, and a straw. Directions can be found in the following video: http://www.sciencecrazy.co.uk/#!Make-a-Model-of-a-Neuron/c1mvs/5556098b0cf298b2d3bd6c56.

Events in Science

Current Events
🕀 Find a current events article relating to the field of anatomy and complete the article summary sheet found on pg. 131 of the Appendix. Once you are done, add the sheet to

the events section of your science notebook.

Historical Figures

- ⊕ Continue to research the life and work of James Watson.

Possible Schedules

Two Days a Week

Day 1	Day 2
☐ Read *CK-12 Biology* Section 22.1. ☐ Add the vocabulary to the glossary section of your science notebook. ☐ Read the background and procedure sections for the week's lab. ☐ Do the current events assignment and add the sheet to the events section of your science notebook.	☐ Read *CK-12 Biology* Section 22.2. ☐ Answer the assigned questions in the reading section of your science notebook. ☐ Do the "Quantitative Analysis of Enzymatic Activity" lab in Late Nite Labs. ☐ Record what you have done in the lab section of your science notebook and complete your lab exam for the week.

Five Days a Week

Day 1	Day 2	Day 3	Day 4	Day 5
☐ Read *CK-12 Biology* Section 22.1. ☐ Add the vocabulary to the glossary section of your science notebook.	☐ Read *CK-12 Biology* Section 22.2. ☐ Answer the assigned questions in the reading section of your science notebook.	☐ Read the background and procedure sections for the week's lab.	☐ Do the "Quantitative Analysis of Enzymatic Activity" lab in Late Nite Labs. ☐ Record what you have done in the lab section of your science notebook.	☐ Complete your lab exam for the week. ☐ Do the optional Hands-on Assignment.

Throughout the Week

☐ Choose one of the Events in Science assignments to do and add your work to the events section of your science notebook.

Week 7 Assignment Sheet - Circulatory, Respiratory, Digestive, and Excretory Systems

Textbook Assignments
Reading
📖 *CK-12 Biology* Sections 23.1, 23.2, 23.3, 23.4

Written
After you finish reading, answer questions #1-3 in section 23.1, questions #1-4 in section 23.2, questions #1,3,5,7,9 in section 23.3, and questions #1-3 in section 23.4. File your work in the reading section of your science notebook. Then, define the following terms in the glossary section of your science notebook:

- ☐ Antigen
- ☐ Atherosclerosis
- ☐ Systemic circulation
- ☐ Asthma
- ☐ Emphysema
- ☐ Pneumonia
- ☐ Body mass index (BMI)
- ☐ Chemical digestion
- ☐ Mechanical digestion
- ☐ Macronutrient
- ☐ Micronutrient
- ☐ Peristalsis
- ☐ Dialysis
- ☐ Nephron

Experiment - Antibiotic Sensitivity
Purpose
The purpose of this lab is to explain how antibiotics work and to use a sensitivity test to determine the susceptibility of bacteria to different substances.

Pre-Reading
🖎 Read the background and procedure sections for the "Antibiotic Sensitivity" lab in Late Nite Labs.

Procedure
✓ Do the lab entitled "Antibiotic Sensitivity" in Late Nite Labs.

Lab Notebook
☞ Write down on a sheet of paper or type out your notes in Late Nite Labs as you do the experiment. After you are done, print out your lab notes and add them to the lab section of your science notebook.

Lab Exam
⚡ Complete the multiple choice section of the "Antibiotic Sensitivity" lab in Late Nite Labs. Submit the grade to your teacher.

Optional Hands-on
✂ This week, dissect a cow's, pig's, or sheep's heart using a kit that you can purchase from Carolina Biological, Rainbow Resources, or Home Science Tools.

Events in Science

Current Events

🕐 Find a current events article relating to the field of anatomy and complete the article summary sheet found on pg. 131 of the Appendix. Once you are done, add the sheet to the events section of your science notebook.

Historical Figures

🕐 Continue to research the life and work of James Watson.

Possible Schedules

Two Days a Week

Day 1	Day 2
❑ Read *CK-12 Biology* Section 23.1 and 23.2. ❑ Add the vocabulary to the glossary section of your science notebook. ❑ Read the background and procedure sections for the week's lab. ❑ Do the current events assignment and add the sheet to the events section of your science notebook.	❑ Read *CK-12 Biology* Section 23.3 and 23.4. ❑ Answer the assigned questions in the reading section of your science notebook. ❑ Do the "Antibiotic Sensitivity" lab in Late Nite Labs. ❑ Record what you have done in the lab section of your science notebook and complete your lab exam for the week.

Five Days a Week

Day 1	Day 2	Day 3	Day 4	Day 5
❑ Read *CK-12 Biology* Section 23.1 and 23.2. ❑ Add the vocabulary to the glossary section of your science notebook.	❑ Read *CK-12 Biology* Section 23.3 and 23.4. ❑ Answer the assigned questions in the reading section of your science notebook.	❑ Read the background and procedure sections for the week's lab.	❑ Do the "Antibiotic Sensitivity" lab in Late Nite Labs. ❑ Record what you have done in the lab section of your science notebook.	❑ Complete your lab exam for the week. ❑ Do the optional Hands-on Assignment.

Throughout the Week

❑ Choose one of the Events in Science assignments to do and add your work to the events section of your science notebook.

Week 8 Assignment Sheet - Immune System

Textbook Assignments

Reading

📖 *CK-12 Biology* Sections 24.1, 24.2, 24.3, 24.4

Written

After you finish reading, answer questions #1-4 in section 24.1, questions #1-4 in section 24.2, questions #1-4 in section 24.3, and questions #1,3,5 in section 24.4. File your work in the reading section of your science notebook. Then, define the following terms in the glossary section of your science notebook:

- [ ] Leukocyte
- [ ] Phagocytosis
- [ ] Active immunity
- [ ] Antibody
- [ ] Passive immunity

- [ ] T-cell
- [ ] Autoimmune disease
- [ ] Immunodeficiency
- [ ] Carcinogen

Experiment - Full Lab Report

Lab Notebook

☞ This week, choose one of your previous labs and begin to write a full lab report. See pg. 113 for directions on how to write a full lab report. You will have two weeks to complete your write-up.

Optional Hands-on

✄ See how viruses and bacteria spread through touching using several different colors of glitter and a few friends. Have each person choose a color of glitter and rub some on their hands. Then, go around shaking each other's hands and observe what happens.

Events in Science

Current Events

🕐 Find a current events article relating to the field of anatomy and complete the article summary sheet found on pg. 131 of the Appendix. Once you are done, add the sheet to the events section of your science notebook.

Historical Figures

🕐 Begin to work on your paper on the life and work of James Watson. This week, aim to complete your outline and rough draft. See pg. 118 in the Appendix for more directions. You will have three weeks to complete this paper.

Possible Schedules

Two Days a Week

Day 1	Day 2
❏ Read *CK-12 Biology* Section 24.1 to 24.4. ❏ Add the vocabulary to the glossary section of your science notebook. ❏ Answer the assigned questions in the reading section of your science notebook. ❏ Do the current events assignment and add the sheet to the events section of your science notebook.	❏ Work on the full Lab Report. ❏ Do the current events assignment and add the sheet to the events section of your science notebook.

Five Days a Week

Day 1	Day 2	Day 3	Day 4	Day 5
❏ Read *CK-12 Biology* Section 24.1 and 24.2. ❏ Add the vocabulary to the glossary section of your science notebook.	❏ Read *CK-12 Biology* Section 24.3 and 24.4. ❏ Answer the assigned questions in the reading section of your science notebook.	❏ Work on the full Lab Report.	❏ Work on the full Lab Report.	❏ Do the optional Hands-on Assignment.

Throughout the Week

❏ Choose one of the Events in Science assignments to do and add your work to the events section of your science notebook.

Week 9 Assignment Sheet - Reproduction

Textbook Assignments
Reading
📖 *CK-12 Biology* Sections 25.1, 25.2, 25,3

Written
After you finish reading, answer questions #1,3,5 in section 25.1, questions #1,3 in section 25.2, and questions #1,3,5 in section 25.3, . File your work in the reading section of your science notebook. Then, define the following terms in the glossary section of your science notebook:

- ☐ Luteinizing hormone
- ☐ Spermatogenesis
- ☐ Oogenesis
- ☐ Blastocyst
- ☐ Fetus
- ☐ Infancy

Experiment - Full Lab Report
Lab Notebook
☞ This week, finish writing the full lab report you began last week. See pg. 113 for directions on how to write a full lab report. Add your completed write-up to your lab notebook.

Optional Hands-on
✂ There is no optional hands-on activity for this week.

Events in Science
Current Events
🕐 Find a current events article relating to the field of anatomy and complete the article summary sheet found on pg. 131 of the Appendix. Once you are done, add the sheet to the events section of your science notebook.

Historical Figures
🕐 Continue to work on your paper on the life and work of James Watson. This week, aim to complete your final draft. See pg. 118 in the Appendix for more directions.

Possible Schedules

Two Days a Week

Day 1	Day 2
❏ Read *CK-12 Biology* Sections 25.1 to 25.3. ❏ Add the vocabulary to the glossary section of your science notebook. ❏ Answer the assigned questions in the reading section of your science notebook.	❏ Finish the full Lab Report. ❏ Do the current events assignment and add the sheet to the events section of your science notebook.

Five Days a Week

Day 1	Day 2	Day 3	Day 4	Day 5
❏ Read *CK-12 Biology* Sections 25.1 and 25.2. ❏ Add the vocabulary to the glossary section of your science notebook.	❏ Read *CK-12 Biology* Sections 25.3. ❏ Add the vocabulary to the glossary section of your science notebook.	❏ Answer the assigned questions in the reading section of your science notebook.	❏ Work on the full Lab Report.	❏ Finish the full Lab Report.

Throughout the Week

❏ Choose one of the Events in Science assignments to do and add your work to the events section of your science notebook.

Unit 4 Test

1. What is one thing animals can do that plants cannot?

   a. Can externally or internally digest food.

   b. Are sessile their entire lives.

   c. Animals can detect external stimuli.

   d. None of the above.

2. An incomplete digestion system contains:

   a. A digestive cavity with one opening

   b. A digestive cavity with two openings

   c. A digestive cavity with four openings

   d. None of the above

3. What two unique features belong to mollusks?

   a. Shell, nerve ring

   b. Mantle, radula

   c. Nerve cord, foot

4. Annelids are similar to other mollusks except:

   a. Closed circulatory system

   b. Excretory system

   c. Complete digestion system

   d. No gills

5. How many discovered arthropods are there on earth?

   a. 1.5 Million

   b. 1 Million

   c. 500,000

   d. 100,000

6. How many existing species of fish are there:

   a. 15,000

   b. 50,000

   c. 28,000

   d. 500

7. What do lampreys have that other bony fish do not?

    a. Large round mouth with teeth

    b. Fins

    c. Scales

    d. Backbone

8. Cartilaginous fish include everything except:

    a. Rays

    b. Sharks

    c. Ratfish

    d. Striped bass

9. Amphibians are:

    a. Ectothermic

    b. Endothermic

    c. Hyperthermic

    d. None of the above

10. What function do reptile scales serve?

    a. Keep them warm

    b. Protection from predators

    c. Prevent oxygen from being absorbed by the skin

    d. Protect them from injury and water loss

11. All modern birds have every one of these except:

    a. Wings

    b. Feathers

    c. Beak

    d. Fur

12. The most common order of birds is:

    a. Perching birds

    b. Land fowl

    c. Shorebirds

    d. Raptors

13. Mammals mainly keep their body warm by the use of:

    a. Fur

    b. Fat

    c. High metabolism rates

    d. Feathers/hair

14. Of all vertebrates, _____ have the largest and most complex brains.

    a. Birds

    b. Bony fish

    c. Mammals

    d. Tunicates

15. A marsupial is a therian mammal in which the embryo is born:

    a. Mature and ready to defend itself

    b. Immature and helpless

    c. None of the above

16. Monotremes reproduce by:

    a. Giving birth to live young

    b. Fertilization occurs outside the parents

    c. Laying eggs

    d. None of the above

17. What is cartilage?

    a. Dense connective tissue

    b. Dense bony tissue

    c. Hollow light bony tissue

18. The three types of muscle cells are all of the following, except:

    a. Smooth

    b. Skeletal

    c. Cardiac

    d. Thoracic

19. The two parts of a sarcomere are the _____ and _____

    a. Actin and Myosin

    b. Myosin and ADP

    c. Actin and Hemoglobin

    d. None of the above

20. What is peristalsis?

    a. Involuntary muscle contraction in the heart

    b. Involuntary muscle contraction that moves along the organ like a wave

    c. Voluntary muscle contraction of the small intestine

    d. None of the above

Biology for the Rhetoric Stage

Appendix

What a full Lab Report should include

It is very important that all students begin to understand the process of writing scientific laboratory reports. Learning technical writing is a skill that must be practiced in order to become proficient. Having your students write laboratory reports also helps them to think critically as they analyzes the data that they have observed in the experiments. It will also give them a good basis for scientific writing that will help to prepare them for college level work.

The Components

Although there are some variations to a scientific lab report depending on the discipline you are writing for, they all contain the same basic components. Below is a general outline of the components of a scientific lab report:

1. Title

2. Abstract

3. Introduction

4. Materials and Procedure

5. Results (includes observations and data)

6. Conclusion

7. Works Cited

Each section of the scientific lab report should include specific information. The following is an explanation of what each section should have.

Title

This section should summarize the scientific experiment in 10 words or less and use key words in the report.

Abstract

An abstract gives a one paragraph synopsis of the research that the scientist has done. Generally, the scientist will write a full research report and the abstract can let the reader know if reading the full report would be beneficial. The abstract should contain the data and conclusions of the report in two hundred words or less. If you have not completed an associated research report, you can use this to summarize their research.

Introduction

The introduction section of the report is designed to give the reader the basis for the report, the reason why it was completed, and the background about what is already known about the experiment. Usually this section answers, "Why did we do this study?", "What information was known before we began the experiment?", and "What is the purpose of the study?"

Materials and Procedures

This section tells the reader what specific equipment and supplies were used in the experiment. You will also need to describe how the equipment and supplies were used. It is also important to describe when and where the experiment was conducted. The purpose of this information is to allow any person that reads the scientific report to be able to replicate the results. Without being able to replicate the results, the data obtained are not confirmable.

Results

The main purpose of the results section is to present the data that were obtained during the experiment. It is important that you present just the data and avoid analyzing or making conclusions about the data, as there is another section for this. The results section is also the place to include tables, graphs, and data tables. These should be easily understood by the average reader and be well labeled.

Conclusion

In the conclusion section you should focus on analyzing the data. Don't just reiterate the data; rather, draw conclusions from the data. It is permissible to draw speculative conclusions; just remember to state that is what you are doing. In this section, you should also discuss if the hypothesis was confirmed or invalidated and if further experimentation should be carried out to refine your hypothesis. You must also discuss any errors that occurred during the lab; these are usually not human errors but rather systematic errors that occur while conducting the experiment. Systematic errors can be caused by improper calibration of equipment, changes in the environment, and estimation errors. In the conclusion, it is important to present these errors that may have occurred in your experiment. This section is usually written in third person, passive, past tense.

Works Cited

This is the listing of the research materials used in the report to give background or to help corroborate the data. All outside sources must be cited. The format you will use for the works cited (i.e., MLA, APA, Turabian etc.) will depend upon the scientific field that this lab report relates to.

The Style

When formatting the lab reports, there are some basic guidelines about style that you should know.

1. Have a one inch margin and use 12pt New Times Roman font.

2. All chemical formulas should be formatted properly (i.e. Cl_2, H_2O)

3. Chemical structures that are drawn should be neat and easily readable.

4. Pay attention to formatting, spelling, and the overall look of the lab report.

More Information on Lab Reports

We recommend two books for your student to better prepare for writing scientific papers and lab reports. These books cover in greater detail what we covered in the previous section and they can be easily obtained from Amazon or your university library.

&⁓ *A Student Handbook For Writing In Biology* by Karin Kinsely

&⁓ *Making Sense: Life Sciences: A Student's Guide to Research and Writing* by Margot Northey

The In-depth Project

For the in-depth project, the student will follow the same steps as they did in the science fair project. However, during the high school years, they will go deeper with each step. For example, in middle school, they may have had only five references, whereas in high school, they will need around fifteen to twenty references for their research. The in-depth project should also be a semester long process, rather than several weeks.

So, let's say the student chooses to do an in-depth project involving hydroponics. They want to know if the use of hydroponics will increase plant yield. Their hypothesis, which is supported by their research, states that "Hydroponics produces a superior yield compared to traditional growing methods." For their experiment, they set up two growing environments—one in potting soil and one using hydroponics. At the middle school level, the students would have only used one type of plant observed over two to three weeks. Now, for the in-depth project, they will use multiple types of plants, such as a flower, a grass, a lettuce, and a vegetable, which they allow to grow for two to three months. The students will still need to record their observations and data daily.

Once their experiment is completed, the students will use their mathematical knowledge to analyze and report their findings. Their conclusions will be much more in depth and will include their own inferences about the findings. Once their project is complete, the student should each give a ten to fifteen minute oral presentation explaining their projects and their results.

More Information

For more information on how to do a science fair project, please read the following:

&ᔿ *The Science Fair Project: A Step-by-Step Guide* by Brad and Paige Hudson
&ᔿ The Science Fair Project Webinar: https://www.youtube.com/watch?v=BBta5U2I7O4

The Research Report

The research report process should take the students about half the year to complete. Begin by having every student pick a topic and research the topic, finding out as much material as they can. They can look in biological abstracts, Google Scholar, reference books, and encyclopedias. As they find information, have them take notes that are separated into subtopics. We recommend that they put the different pieces of information on index cards that are numbered for each reference and subtopic. However, if you want the students to use a computer program rather than hand–written notes, we recommend RefWorks, which is widely used as a reference software in colleges today.

The next step is to have the students write their thesis statements. The purpose of the thesis statement is to give a focus to the paper. Their statements should give their point of view or slant on the topic. You can ask them the following questions to help them craft a thesis statement:

- What do you know currently about the topic?
- What are questions that you have about the topic?
- How do you feel about the topic?

This is a fluid process, so their thesis statements may need to be revised several times before the first draft is written.

After the students have written their thesis statements, they each needs to create an outline for their papers from the information that they gathered. Their papers needs to have three sections:

1. Introduction – This section gives a brief look at the topic, states their thesis statement, and explains why they choose the topic.

2. Body – This is the main part of their paper and contains multiple paragraphs full of information that supports the thesis statement. The body should include several quotes from experts or excerpts from their research that give credence to the thesis statement about the topic.

3. Conclusion – This section will restate the thesis statement, summarize the supporting information, and apply it to today.

After you have approved their outline, have each student turn in a rough draft of the paper. If they are not familiar with writing research papers, you may want to have them turn in multiple drafts. Either way, the final research report should be six to eight pages in length (double-spaced). You are looking to make sure that the paper is written in the third person, that it uses the correct MLA style documentation, and that the paper has a strong thesis statement with good supporting evidence.

The Scientist Biography Report

Step 1 - Research

Begin by looking for a biography on the scientist at the library. Then, look for articles on the chemist in magazines, newspapers, encyclopedias, or on the Internet. You will need to know the following about your scientist to write your report:

📖 Biographical information on the scientist (i.e., where they were born, their parents, siblings, and how they grew up);

📖 The scientist's education (i.e., where they went to school, what kind of student they were, what they studied, and so on);

📖 Their scientific contributions (i.e., research that they participated in, any significant discoveries they made, and the state of the world at the time of their contributions).

As you read over the material you have gathered, be sure to write down any facts you glean in your own words. You can do this on the sheet below or on separate index cards. You can read more about this method by clicking below:

💻 http://elementalblogging.com/the-index-card-system/

Step 2 - Create an Outline

Now that your research is completed, you are ready to begin the process of writing a report on your chosen scientist. You are going to organize the notes you took during step two into a formal outline, which you will use next week to write the rough draft of your report. Use the outline template provided on the student sheets as a guide. You should include information on why you chose the particular scientist in your introduction section. For the conclusion section of the outline, you need to include why you believe someone else should learn about your chosen scientist and your impression of the scientist (i.e., Did you like the scientist? Do you feel that they made a significant impact on the field of chemistry?).

The outline you create can look like the one below:

<u>Scientist Biography Outline</u>

I. Introduction & Biological Information on the Scientist (4-6 points)

II. The Scientist's Education (4-6 points)

III. The Scientist's Contributions (1-3 sub categories each with 4-5 points)

IV. Conclusion (4-5 points)

Step 3 - Write a Rough Draft

In the last step, you created a formal outline for your scientist biography report; now, it is time to take that outline and turn it into a rough draft. Simply take the points on your outline, combine them, and add in sentence openers to create a cohesive paragraph. Here's what your rough draft should look like:

📖 Paragraph 1 (from outline point I): introduce the scientist;

📖 Paragraph 2 (from outline point II): tell about the scientist's education;

📖 Paragraph 3-5 (from outline point III): share the scientist's contributions (one paragraph for each contribution);

📖 Paragraph 6 (from outline point IV): share your thoughts on the scientist and why someone should learn about him or her.

You can choose to hand write or type up your rough draft on a separate sheet of paper. However, keep in mind that you will need a typed version for the final step.

Step 5- Revise to Create a Final Draft

Now that you have a typed, double-spaced rough draft, look over it one more time to make any changes you would like. Then, have your teacher or one of your peers look over the paper for you to correct any errors and bring clarity to any of the unclear sections. Once this is complete, make the necessary changes to your paper to create your final draft.

Adding Current Events into your Science Studies

Step 1 - Choose the article.

The first step is to choose an appropriate article. Usually, I try to pick one from the field of science that we are studying. You can subscribe to a kid's science magazine, do a Google search, or check out our Science News for Students to find possible articles. Once you have collected a list of options, peruse through them and pick one that you think will interest your student.

Step 2 - Read the article.

The next step is to have the students read the actual article. Simply hand them the article and tell each of them to come see you when they are done reading it.

Step 3 - Discuss the article.

The third step is to discuss the article the student is reading. I typically ask questions like:

- What was the article about?
- What do you think about (a piece of research or an experiment that the article pointed out)?
- How does the article relate to (something that we have studied on the subject)?
- Did you find the article to be interesting?
- Do you agree with the opinion(s) stated in the article?

Step 4 - Write a summary.

The final step to adding current events to your science students is to have each student write a summary. Once you finish the discussion, ask your students to write three to five sentences on the article, including their opinion on it. Since you have already talked about the piece, this step is easy for the students to do.

Optional Hands-on Experiments Supply List

Unit 1: Cell Structure, Function, and Reproduction

Week	Supplies Needed
1	Microscope, Blank slides, Various materials to examine
2	Lego bricks
3	Red cabbage juice or pH paper, Common household chemicals such as bleach, ammonia, and vinegar
4	Jell-O, Margarine container, Grape, Other materials for organelles
5	Gummy bears, Glass, Water
6	Leaf, Bowl, Water
7	Bowl, Water, Sugar, Yeast
8	Chicken egg
9	Pipe cleaners, Poster board
10	Pipe cleaners, Poster board

Unit 2: Genetics and Evolution

Week	Supplies Needed
1	Legos
2	Easter eggs, M&M's
3	Types of food, such as a banana or a slice of bread
4	Family pictures, Poster board
5	*No supplies needed.*
6	Sheet of paper, Pencil
7	*No supplies needed.*

Unit 3: Ecology, Eukaryotes, and Plant Life

Week	Supplies Needed
1	Sheet of paper, Pencil
2	*No supplies needed.*
3	*No supplies needed.*
4	Swabs, Petri dishes, Agar
5	Gloves, Trowel, Magnifying glass or hand-held microscope
6	Magnifying glass or hand-held microscope, Putty knife
7	Flower, Razor, Magnifying glass, Q-tip, Blank slide, Microscope

8	Onion, Glass, Water, Blank slide, Stain, Microscope
9	Large clear jar, Aquarium pebbles or other small rocks, Activated charcoal, Potting soil, Moss

Unit 4: Animals and the Human Body

Week	Supplies Needed
1	Starfish dissection kit
2	Worm farm kit or Glass jar, Potting soil, Crushed leaves, Worms
3	Perch dissection kit
4	*No supplies needed.*
5	Pool noodle, Washers, Hair ties, Nylon rope
6	Pom-poms, Pipe cleaners, Straw
7	Heart dissection kit
8	Glitter, A few friends
9	*No supplies needed.*

Biology for the Rhetoric Stage

Grading Resources

Answers to the Unit Tests

Unit Test 1 Answers

1. D
2. A
3. C
4. D
5. A
6. C
7. C
8. D
9. A
10. A

11. D
12. D
13. A
14. C
15. A
16. D
17. A
18. B
19. D
20. A

Unit Test 2 Answers

1. C
2. A
3. B
4. A
5. A
6. D
7. D
8. A
9. A

10. A
11. A
12. C
13. D
14. A
15. A
16. A
17. A
18. C

Unit Test 3 Answers

1. C
2. C
3. D
4. D
5. C
6. A
7. B
8. B
9. C
10. A

11. D
12. C
13. C
14. A
15. C
16. D
17. B
18. A
19. C
20. B

Unit Test 4 Answers

1. C	13. C
2. A	14. C
3. B	15. B
4. D	16. C
5. A	17. A
6. C	18. D
7. A	19. A
8. D	20. B
9. A	
10. D	
11. D	
12. A	

Scientist Biography Report Grading Rubric

Spelling (points x 1)

4 points: No spelling mistakes.

3 points: 1-2 spelling mistakes and not distracting to the reader.

2 points: 3-4 spelling mistakes and somewhat distracting.

1 point: 5 spelling mistakes and somewhat distracting.

0 points: > 5 spelling mistakes and no proofreading obvious.

Points Earned _____

Grammar (points x 1)

4 points: No grammatical mistakes.

3 points: 1-2 grammatical mistakes and not distracting to the reader.

2 points: 3-4 grammatical mistakes and somewhat distracting.

1 point: 5 grammatical mistakes and somewhat distracting.

0 points: > 5 grammatical mistakes and no proofreading obvious.

Points Earned _____

Introduction to the Scientist (points x 2)

4 points: Includes thorough summary of the scientist's biographical information and why the student chose the particular scientist.

3 points: Adequate summary of the scientist's biographical information and why the student chose the particular scientist.

2 points: Inaccurate or incomplete summary of one of the scientist's biographical information and why the student chose the particular scientist.

1 point: Inaccurate or incomplete summary of both of the scientist's biographical information and why the student chose the particular scientist.

0 points: No introduction

Points Earned _____

Description of the Scientist's Education (points x 2)

4 points: Includes thorough summary of the scientist's education.

3 points: Adequate summary of the scientist's education.

2 points: Inaccurate or incomplete summary of one of the scientist's education.

1 point: Inaccurate or incomplete summary of both of the scientist's education.

0 points: No description of the scientist's education.

Points Earned _____

Description of the Scientist's Major Contributions (points x 2)

4 points: Includes thorough summary of the scientist's major contributions.

3 points: Adequate summary of the scientist's major contributions.

2 points: Inaccurate or incomplete summary of the scientist's major contributions.

1 point: Inaccurate and incomplete summary of the scientist's major contributions.

0 points: No description of the scientist's major contributions and interesting facts of their life.

Points Earned _____

Conclusion (points x 2)

4 points: Explanation of why the student feels one should study the scientist and a summary statement about the scientist.

3 points: Adequate explanation of why the student feels one should study the scientist and a summary statement about the scientist.

2 points: Incomplete or incorrect explanation of why the student feels one should study the scientist and a summary statement about the scientist.

1 point: Conclusion does not have an explanation of why the student feels one should study the scientist and a summary statement about the scientist.

0 points: No conclusion.

Points Earned _____

Final Score = (Total Points/40) x 100%

Total Points Earned _____

Final Score _____

Biology for the Rhetoric Stage

Templates

Science in the News

Date: _____

Headline: _____
_____

Authored by: _____

My Summary: _____
_____
_____
_____
_____
_____
_____
_____
_____
_____
_____
_____
_____
_____
_____

My Thoughts: _____
_____
_____
_____
_____
_____
_____

Made in the USA
Columbia, SC
23 July 2018